D0987209

The Electronic Structure of Molecules

The Electronic Structure of Molecules

A NEW APPROACH

by

J. W. LINNETT F.R.S.

LONDON: METHUEN & CO LTD
NEW YORK: JOHN WILEY & SONS INC

First published in 1964

Printed in Great Britain by
Spottiswoode Ballantyne & Co Ltd
London & Colchester
Catalogue No. (*Methuen*) 12/2235/63

Preface

In 1961 the American Chemical Society published in its Journal a paper by the author which was entitled 'A Modification of the Lewis–Langmuir Octet Rule'. This book contains a fuller presentation of the proposals put forward there and in other papers; in particular, it extends the suggested structures to a wider range of examples. This approach to the subject of chemical binding is essentially qualitative, though it seeks to use the hypothesis proposed to extend the understanding of the variation in properties in groups of related molecules and ions. Also, because it provides a means of constructing wave functions, numerical calculations are possible and are being developed.

This is a description of one particular method of formulating the electronic structures of molecules; it is not intended to provide a comparison with others which are used such as, for example, that which employs molecular orbitals. In a few places reference has been made to, and comparison has been made with, other methods, but such references are incidental to the main purpose of the book. A more general examination of different ways of describing the electronic structures of molecules will be given by the author elsewhere; the various methods will then be compared.

The approach in this book is to use fundamental physical effects such as the electrostatic repulsion of electrons, the attraction of electrons by nuclei, the consequent tendency to achieve a fairly uniform charge distribution, the effect of the spin wave function on the space distribution of electrons, and similar physical effects, to account for electronic structures in molecular systems, and to explain the resulting properties. Efforts have been made either to eliminate phrases such as 'attainment of the octet', 'stabilization by resonance', 'exchange forces', 'hybridization', etc., or to explain the reasons for them so that their use may be based on understandable physical principles.

This book is intended to describe the basic content of the hypothesis proposed, but it is not intended to be a final statement of the way this method is to be applied to the structure of all the molecules included in the book, and there will no doubt be modifications to be made. It will be clear to the reader that some of the discussions are more firmly based than others. The more tentative applications have been included to indicate ways in which the use of this hypothesis might develop; this would seem to be justifiable considering the purpose.

It is true that this hypothesis has already been advanced in papers in scientific journals, but it has become increasingly clear to the author that these do not provide a suitable vehicle for its presentation; it is felt that a book which can gather together a much wider range of material is much more suitable.

I want to thank the many collaborators who have contributed their help over the last few years in the development of this hypothesis and have carried out calculations based on it. They are: A. J. Poë, C. E. Mellish, P. G. Dickens, M. Green, D. M. Hirst, J. D. Hopton, O. Sovers, R. E. Townshend, M. Barber, J. Farren, P. B. Empedocles, H. C. Bowen, G. Frank, R. D. Gould, J. W. May, M. H. Booth, R. Heckingbottom, R. M. Rosenberg, W. H. Kirchhoff, and D. P. Chong. I wish to express my heartfelt gratitude to many friends in the Chemistry Department at the University of California for giving me their encouragement and criticism in such a generous and stimulating manner. I would like to record my particular debt to R. E. Powell for his ideas and interest, for giving me heart by using this approach in his Freshman lectures in 1960, and for discussing the symbolism to be used. I wish also to record my grateful thanks to R. M. Acheson, R. P. Bell, E. J. Bowen and C. A. Coulson for their advice and encouragement.

Finally I would like to thank the others who have helped me to write this book; in particular, my wife for seeing that I had the time and for giving me her support, and Mrs Hoare for the speed with which she typed the manuscript, for her skill in reading my writing, and for her helpful comments on the text. I am also grateful to D. P. Chong for his help with the proofs and with the index.

Contents

To

G. N. LEWIS,

N. V. SIDGWICK and L. PAULING

as a mark of respect

for the contributions

made by them

to this subject

CHAPTER ONE

Electrons and Atoms

1.1 Introduction

Modern theories of valency and the structure of atoms and molecules may be considered to arise directly from the discovery of the electron in 1895 and the proposal of the quantum theory by Planck in 1900.

The negatively charged electron was soon shown to be a universal constituent of matter, and speculation as to the nature of the positively charged part of the atom followed. Largely as a result of the work of Rutherford and his collaborators at Manchester, it was concluded that it was small and heavy, relative to the electron. As a result, the atom came to be regarded as a minute *solar system* in which a number of electrons revolved round a nucleus which carried a charge equal to that of the planetary electrons. The work of Moseley on characteristic X-ray spectra suggested that the number of planetary electrons (and therefore the charge on the nucleus) was to be identified with the atomic number, and this was confirmed by careful experiments on the scattering of beams of α particles by thin films of gold, platinum and copper.

The quantum theory was proposed by Planck to explain the energy distribution in black-body radiation. It was developed further by Einstein who applied it to the specific heats of solids and to the photo-electric effect. Other applications followed. Planck proposed that energy could be transferred by electromagnetic radiation of frequency ν only in packets of magnitude E, where

$$E = h\nu. \qquad 1.1$$

In this equation, h is a universal constant equal to $6 \cdot 623 \times 10^{-27}$ erg-sec known as Planck's constant. Einstein suggested that, for particles undergoing vibrational motion, the energy they could possess was also quantized. Bohr applied the quantum theory to atoms. Following Rutherford's proposal of the nuclear atom, it had been supposed that the frequencies of the radiation emitted by atoms must be associated with the frequencies of the motion of the negatively charged electrons round the positively charged nucleus. Classically this system would be expected to emit radiation. However, this leads to the difficulty that the atom will continuously lose energy as radiation, so that the electron will not be stable in its orbit but will ultimately spiral into the nucleus. Bohr concluded that an electron in its orbit must be stable, retaining its energy without continuous loss. He said that the system was capable of existing in a number of 'stationary' states having, let us say, energies E_1, E_2, E_3 ... in which the electrons revolved in orbits of unchanging size. Secondly, he proposed that when an atom emitted (or absorbed) radiation, it passed from one stationary state to another, the difference of energy providing (or being provided by) a quantum of radiation. This requires, using 1.1, that the frequency of the radiation is given by

$$\Delta E = E_1 - E_2 = h\nu. \tag{1.2}$$

These two suggestions by Bohr revolutionized the interpretation of spectra and, because of them, it was possible to use spectroscopic data to make far-reaching conclusions regarding the electronic structure of atoms. They are two of the most important contributions that have ever been made in the physical sciences.

1.2 The Hydrogen Atom

The spectrum and energy levels of the hydrogen atom will be considered first because it contains just *one* electron in addition to the positively charged nucleus, and therefore its spectrum is the simplest of all atomic

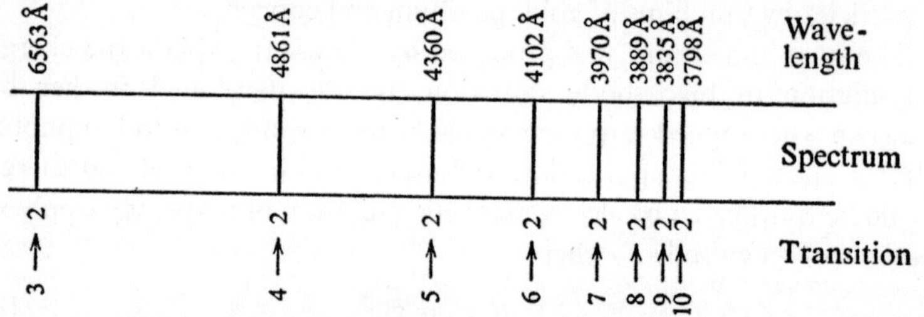

FIG. 1. Balmer series in the spectrum of atomic hydrogen.

spectra. A study of the spectrum of the hydrogen atom, obtained from a discharge tube containing hydrogen at low pressures, shows that there are present a number of lines which are grouped together in several well-defined sequences. For instance, across the visible and near ultra-violet region, there is such a series in which the lines are widely spaced at the long wave-length end but converge towards a limit in the near ultra-violet. A diagram of this, known as the Balmer series, is shown in Fig. 1.

In the far ultra-violet there is another series, named after Lyman, and there are several others in the red end of the visible region and in the near infra-red. It is found that the frequencies of all the lines in the atomic spectrum of hydrogen are given very accurately by the formula

$$\nu = R\left[\frac{1}{n^2} - \frac{1}{m^2}\right], \tag{1.3}$$

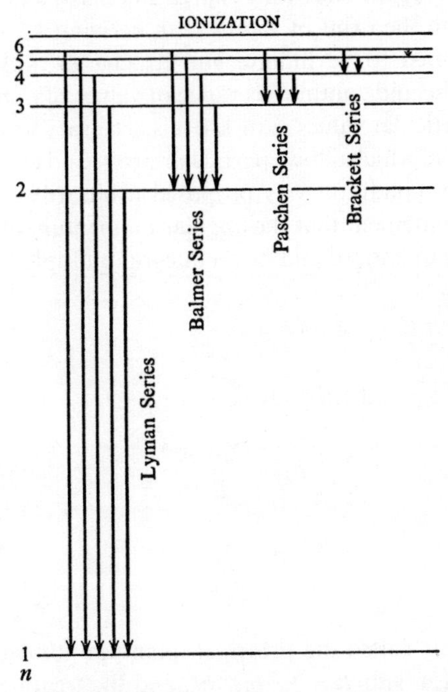

FIG. 2. Energy levels of the hydrogen atom showing also some observed transitions.

where R is a constant (the Rydberg constant) and n and m are integers. For the Lyman series $n = 1$ and $m = 2, 3, 4 \ldots$; for the Balmer series $n = 2$ and $m = 3, 4, 5 \ldots$; and similarly for the other series. A comparison of 1.2 and 1.3 suggests that the energy levels E_n are given by

$$E_n = Rh\left[\frac{1}{n^2}\right] \tag{1.4}$$

(1.1 is used to convert from frequency in 1.3 to energy in 1.4). A diagram of these energy levels, together with the way in which the various series of lines arise from transitions between the levels, is shown in Fig. 2.

Bohr supposed that the electrons revolved in circular orbits, and treated the motion in these orbits classically. The energy, radius of the orbit, and velocity of the electron in the orbit are related by

$$E = -\frac{e^2}{2r} = -\frac{1}{2}mv^2 \qquad 1.5$$

where $-e$ and m are the electronic charge and mass, and v is the velocity of the electron in the orbit of radius r (in deriving 1.5 the mass of the nucleus is assumed to be infinite and its charge $+e$). Equation 1.5 permits an infinite and continuous range of values of r and v. To restrict the energy to particular values as in 1.4, it is necessary to apply a *so-called quantum condition*, which allows particular orbits and excludes all others. Such a quantum condition was proposed arbitrarily by Bohr. It was equivalent to a statement that the angular momentum of the electron in its orbit must be quantized and be an integral multiple of $h/2\pi$. That is

$$mvr = n.\frac{h}{2\pi}. \qquad 1.6$$

Combination of 1.5 and 1.6 gives

$$E_n = \frac{2\pi^2 me^4}{n^2 h^2}, \qquad 1.7$$

and

$$r = \frac{n^2 h^2}{4\pi^2 me^2}. \qquad 1.8$$

The constant n is called the principal quantum number. Formula 1.7 corresponds to 1.4 with $R = 2\pi^2 me^4/h^3$, and the treatment leads to the result that the electron is limited to circular orbits of radii a_0, $4a_0$, $9a_0$, $16a_0$, etc., where $a_0 = h^2/4\pi^2 me^2$, and is known as the Bohr radius ($a_0 = 0{\cdot}53$ Å).

Sommerfeld developed the treatment of Bohr and included elliptical orbits. For circular orbits the principal quantum number n defined both the energy (by 1.7) and the angular momentum (by 1.6). If elliptical orbits are allowed, it is possible for the angular momentum and energy to be quantized independently. That is, there were two quantum numbers k and n. The former defines the quantized angular momentum by

$$\text{angular momentum} = k\frac{h}{2\pi}; \qquad 1.9$$

k was called the azimuthal quantum number. The energy is still given by 1.7. The energy of an elliptical orbit is dependent on the length of the major axis which is $n^2h^2/2\pi^2me^2$ (i.e. $n^2a_0^2$), independent of k. For elliptical orbits the angular momentum is less than that for the circular orbit of the same energy. Therefore k must always be less than or equal to n, and, in fact, the length of the minor axis is k/n times that of the major axis. The three orbits for which $n = 3$ are illustrated in Fig. 3; k is 1, 2 or 3.

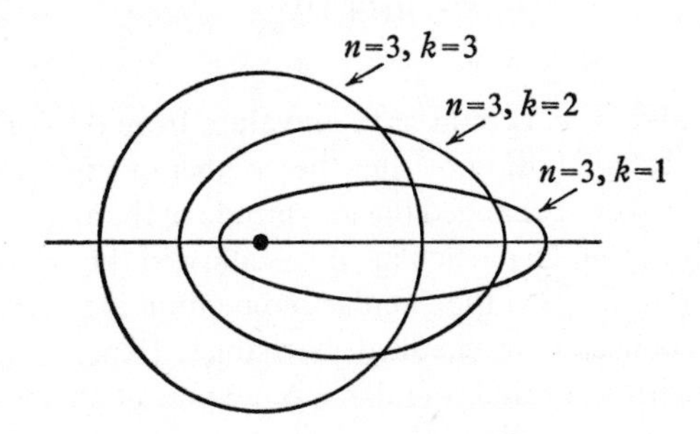

FIG. 3. Bohr–Sommerfeld orbits for $n = 3$.

1.3 Quantum Mechanics and Orbitals

The Bohr–Sommerfeld treatment, while being correct in focusing attention on the importance of the separate quantization of energy and of angular momentum, and also in certain respects in the pattern of quantum numbers, was incorrect in detail. In particular it was incorrect quantitatively regarding the magnitude of the allowed quantized values of the angular momentum. These difficulties were remedied by the advent of quantum mechanics in 1926. Some early workers described this new method as quantum dynamics, and perhaps this provides a better description because the treatment of motion and momentum is particularly affected.

The precursor of quantum mechanics was de Broglie's suggestion in 1924 that, like radiation, matter possessed a wave-particle duality of behaviour, the relationship for which was

$$mv = \frac{h}{\lambda}, \qquad 1.10$$

where mv is the momentum of the particle and λ the wave-length. This applies to a particle moving with constant momentum; that is, in a region in which its potential energy (V) remains constant. Schrödinger extended de Broglie's idea so that it could be applied to systems in which V varied with the position of the particle or particles. When this was applied to the hydrogen atom it was found that Sommerfeld's quantum number, k, had to be replaced by an alternative one, l, which was one less than k. This was called the subsidiary quantum number, and the resultant angular momentum associated with a given value of l is

$$\sqrt{[l(l+1)]}\frac{h}{2\pi}. \tag{1.11}$$

For a given value of n, l could have all values from 0 to $(n-1)$.

Quantum mechanics did not alter the number of sub-levels for a given value of n. However, it changed the magnitude of the angular momentum associated with each. In particular, it has allowed the existence of states of the electron, for which the angular momentum is zero ($l=0$). Such a possibility cannot exist in classical mechanics. Experiment shows that states for which the orbital angular momentum of the electron is zero do exist.

In quantum mechanics the orbits of the Bohr-Sommerfeld semi-classical methods are replaced by orbitals. Quantum mechanics is essentially statistical in character dealing in probabilities and not in the determined trajectories of classical mechanics. It makes use of a function ψ. In the de Broglie situation this is the quantity that varies in a wave-like manner, its wave-length λ being related to the momentum by 1.10. ψ itself has no physical significance, but ψ^2 measures a probability. Thus, for a hydrogen atom in a given state ψ is a particular function of the position of the electron, and for each position of the electron, ψ^2 measures the probability of finding the electron at that place.

Figure 4 shows diagrammatically the angular variation of ψ for $l=0$, 1 and 2, corresponding to $k=1$, 2 and 3 in Fig. 3. For $n=3$, the $l=0$ function would be multiplied by a radial function varying with r, the distance from the nucleus, which had two nodes (i.e. it may be considered, rather approximately, as made up of 3 half-waves). The $l=1$ function would be multiplied by one having 1 node, and the $l=2$ by one having no nodes. These are shown in Fig. 5. The $l=0$ function has no angular momentum because there is no variation in ψ with angle at a fixed distance from the nucleus (cf. λ is infinite for the de Broglie wave). On the other hand, of the three orbits, it has the most radial (in–out) momentum (3 half-waves). An electron in the $n=3$, $l=1$ orbital has less radial momentum (2 half-waves) but it has angular momentum. Traversing any circle round either the x axis or the y axis there is one full wave (ψ goes from zero to plus to zero to minus and back to zero). This means in fact that about these axes the electron possesses one unit of angular momentum $[1.(h/2\pi)]$. Because there is no angular variation around the z axis,

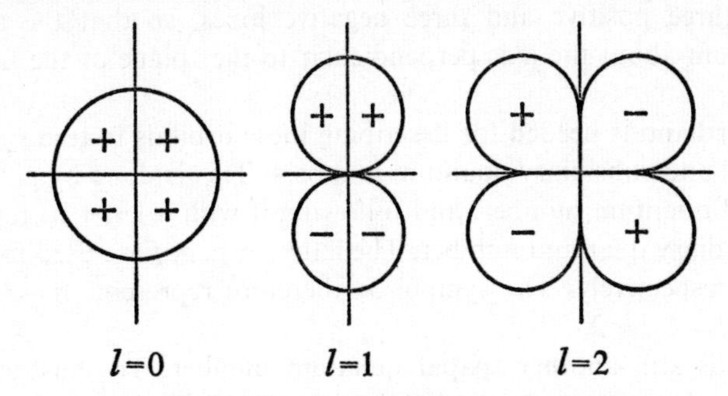

FIG. 4. Diagrammatic representation of the angular variation of the wave functions for which $l=0$, $l=1$, $l=2$.

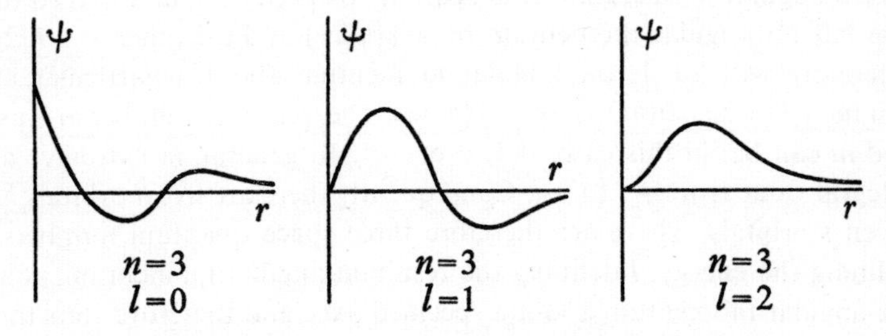

FIG. 5. Variation of ψ with r, the distance from the nucleus, for the $3s$, $3p$ and $3d$ orbitals.

the angular momentum about this axis is zero. The resultant angular momentum is therefore, by vector addition,

$$\sqrt{\left(1\frac{h^2}{4\pi^2}+1\frac{h^2}{4\pi^2}+0\frac{h^2}{4\pi^2}\right)} = \sqrt{2}\frac{h}{2\pi}.$$

This is $\sqrt{[l(l+1)]}(h/2\pi)$ with $l=1$ (cf. equation 1.11). By a similar argument it can be seen that, for the $l=2$ orbital, the electronic angular momenta about the three perpendicular axes are 2, 1, 1 in units of $h/2\pi$ (2 about the axis perpendicular to the page and 1 about two axes at right angles in the plane of the page). So the resultant is $\sqrt{(6)}(h/2\pi)$, which fits equation 1.11 with $l=2$.

The general form of other orbitals with other values of n and l can be readily visualized. The number of spherical nodes in the radial function is $n-l-1$. The number of non-spherical nodes is l, as can be seen in Fig. 4. One function for $l=3$ is similar to that for $l=2$ shown in Fig. 4 but having three positive and three negative lobes, so that the angular momentum about the axis perpendicular to the 'plane of the lobes' is $3.(h/2\pi)$.

A shorthand is needed for describing these orbitals in terms of their principal and subsidiary quantum numbers. This is done by giving the principal quantum number, and following it with a letter to represent the subsidiary quantum number. The letters *s*, *p*, *d*, *f* are used for $l=0$, 1, 2, 3, respectively. The symbol 3*s* therefore represents $n=3$, $l=0$, and 4*d*, $n=4$, $l=2$.

There is still another spatial quantum number. To illustrate this, *p* orbitals (Fig. 4) may be used. There are three independent *p* orbitals, with the lobes along three perpendicular axes. About a given axis two of these will have an angular momentum of 1 unit, and the other will have a zero angular momentum. It is possible to specify the first two so that one has an angular momentum of $+1(h/2\pi)$ and the other $-1(h/2\pi)$. Therefore with $l=1$, the angular momentum about a particular axis can be $+1(h/2\pi)$, $0(h/2\pi)$, or $-1(h/2\pi)$. The quantum number m is used and m can be, in this case, $+1$, 0 or -1. In general, m can have any integral value from $-l$ to $+l$. Consequently there are five *d* orbitals and seven *f* orbitals. There are therefore three space quantum numbers: n defining the energy, l defining the resultant angular momentum, and m the angular momentum about a specified axis, and therefore something about the orientation of the orbital.

1.4 Electron Spin

There is still one further quantum number. The need for this is shown by consideration of the sodium D-lines at 5890 and 5896 Å. These arise in emission from a transition of an electron from a 3*p* orbital to a 3*s* orbital. The reason why there are two lines is that the electron has an *intrinsic* angular momentum and associated magnetic moment. They are described as the spin angular momentum and spin magnetic moment, because, in pictorial terms, the way in which a charged particle can have an intrinsic magnetic moment is by spinning. As with orbital angular momentum the alignment of this spin magnetic momentum with respect to a specified direction is quantized. In this case a direction is specified by the magnetic field provided by the orbital motion, and there are two allowed alignments of the spin magnetic moment relative to the orbital magnetic moment. Hence the atom with the electron in the $3p$ orbital can have two energies which, in this case, do not differ very much, because the energy of interaction of the two magnetic moments is small. This magnetic interaction increases with increasing charge on the nucleus.

It is found by spectroscopic experience that the spin angular momentum of the electron about a particular direction must be

$$+\frac{1}{2}\cdot\frac{h}{2\pi} \quad \text{or} \quad -\frac{1}{2}\cdot\frac{h}{2\pi}.$$

The spin quantum number (s) of the electron can be plus or minus a half.

1.5 Polyelectronic Atoms

The most important factor governing the electronic structures of the ground states of polyelectronic atoms is the effect summarized in the Pauli Principle. This states that there cannot be two electrons in the same atom with all four quantum numbers the same. Since each spatial orbital is defined by the three quantum numbers n, l and m, this is equivalent to saying that each orbital can accommodate two electrons, and these only if they have different spin quantum numbers. We will consider now the simple consequences of this.

In the ground state of the hydrogen atom the electron occupies the $1s$ orbital. If the nuclear charge is 2 and the atom contains two electrons, these will occupy the $1s$ orbital but with spin quantum numbers of $+\frac{1}{2}$ and $-\frac{1}{2}$ in the lowest state. This is helium. The lithium atom contains three electrons. The third cannot be added to the $1s$ orbital which is already 'full' on the basis of the Pauli Principle. In the ground state it must therefore occupy an orbital with $n=2$. Spectroscopic measurements have shown that, in polyelectronic atoms, an electron in a $2s$ orbital has a lower energy than one in a $2p$ orbital. The structure of the ground state of lithium is $1s^2 2s$ (i.e. two electrons in the $1s$ and one in the $2s$ orbital). As would be expected, the ground state of beryllium is $1s^2 2s^2$, and of boron $1s^2 2s^2 2p$. These structures are summarized in Table 1 which also covers all the elements with atomic numbers (i.e. number of electrons) less than, or equal to, 36.

The addition of a sixth electron in carbon results in the presence of two electrons to be accompanied in the $2p$ orbitals. Clearly, for the

TABLE 1

El.	1*s*	2*s*	$2p_{+1}$	$2p_0$	$2p_{-1}$	3*s*	$3p_{+1}$	$3p_0$	$3p_{-1}$	El.	Inner shells	$3d_{+2}$	$3d_{+1}$	$3d_0$	$3d_{-1}$	$3d_{-2}$	4*s*	$4p_{+1}$	$4p_0$	$4p_{-1}$
H	1									K	18						1			
He	2									Ca	18						2			
Li	2	1								Sc	18	1					2			
Be	2	2								Ti	18	1	1				2			
B	2	2	1							V	18	1	1	1			2			
C	2	2	1	1						Cr	18	1	1	1	1	1	1			
N	2	2	1	1	1					Mn	18	1	1	1	1	1	2			
O	2	2	2	1	1					Fe	18	2	1	1	1	1	2			
F	2	2	2	2	1					Co	18	2	2	1	1	1	2			
Ne	2	2	2	2	2					Ni	18	2	2	2	1	1	2			
Na	2	2	2	2	2	1				Cu	18	2	2	2	2	2	1			
Mg	2	2	2	2	2	2				Zn	18	2	2	2	2	2	2			
Al	2	2	2	2	2	2	1			Ga	18	2	2	2	2	2	2	1		
Si	2	2	2	2	2	2	1	1		Ge	18	2	2	2	2	2	2	1	1	
P	2	2	2	2	2	2	1	1	1	As	18	2	2	2	2	2	2	1	1	1
S	2	2	2	2	2	2	2	1	1	Se	18	2	2	2	2	2	2	2	1	1
Cl	2	2	2	2	2	2	2	2	1	Br	18	2	2	2	2	2	2	2	2	1
A	2	2	2	2	2	2	2	2	2	Kr	18	2	2	2	2	2	2	2	2	2

lowest energy state, it is advantageous to reduce inter-electron repulsion as much as possible. Therefore the two electrons occupy two different $2p$ orbitals as shown in the table. Similarly, in the nitrogen atom, three electrons occupy separately the three $2p$ orbitals. From oxygen to neon electrons are added to fill the $2p$ orbitals. From sodium to argon the $3s$ and $3p$ orbitals are filled in an analogous manner. The next electron (in potassium) might have been expected to occupy the $3d$ orbital. However, if the ion K^+ takes up an electron, the atom has a lower energy if it occupies the $4s$ orbital than if it occupies the $3d$ orbital. Similarly the electronic structure of the calcium atom is $1s^2 2s^2 2p^6 3s^2 3p^6 4s^2$.

In polyelectronic atoms the energy of the orbitals having a given n are lower the smaller the l quantum number; $2s$ is lower than $2p$; $3s$ is

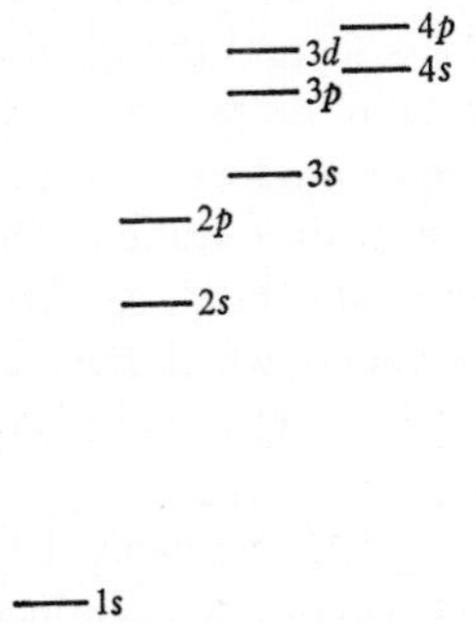

4p
3d
4s
3p
3s
2p
2s
1s

FIG. 6. Order of atomic energy levels.

lower than $3p$, which is lower than $3d$; $4s$ is lower than $4p$, which is lower than $4d$, which is lower than $4f$. The exact relative position of these levels on an energy scale is dependent on the number of electrons present, but the broad situation as regards the order is shown in Fig. 6. The reason why the orbitals having the same n differ in energy (whereas in the hydrogen atom they have the same energy) is that the spatial distribution is dependent on l; and, in particular, the radial function is dependent on l. Because of these differences, the effects of inter-electron repulsion are different, and, as a consequence, the energy is dependent on l. In the hydrogen atom, in which no other electrons are present, the energy is not dependent on l. Therefore the scale in Fig. 6 is taking account, in an empirical way, for the effects of inter-electron repulsion.

A result of the order of levels shown in Fig. 6 is that the extra electron in scandium (following calcium) occupies the $3d$ orbital. In titanium and vanadium the extra electrons are added to other $3d$ orbitals. At chromium a most instructive phenomenon occurs; the six electrons in excess of the argon structure occupy the five separate $3d$ orbitals and the $4s$ orbital. Up to this point, the view has been taken that it is possible to state which orbital of a given pair has the lower energy. This is in a sense true, but our concern here is with the total energy of electronic system of the atom. It is a convenient and useful approximation to treat the energy as made up of a sum of intrinsic orbital energies, each characteristic of a single electron in a particular orbital, together with a sum of inter-electron repulsion energies measuring the energy of interaction of the different electrons. In the case of vanadium, it seems that the relative intrinsic energies of the $4s$ and $3d$ orbitals are sufficient to outweigh the repulsion energy between the two electrons in the $4s$ orbital, which is considerable because they occupy the same spatial orbital. In chromium the reverse seems to be the case, and the six electrons are spread among the five $3d$ and one $4s$ orbital to reduce the effect of inter-electron repulsion. The pattern from manganese to nickel is straightforward. The situation in copper shows how little is the difference between the energy of occupation of a $4s$ and a $3d$ orbital, and that it is dependent on the nuclear charge, and on the way in which the other orbitals are occupied. The pattern from zinc to krypton repeats the earlier ones from beryllium to neon, and from magnesium to argon.

The electronic structures of the elements beyond krypton follow the same general pattern. They will not be examined here because this book will not be concerned with them.

1.6 Charge and Spin Correlation of Electrons

The word 'correlation' is used in this context to mean the mutual effect that particles, in particular electrons, have on one another's spatial positions. By charge correlation we mean the effect that electrons have on one another by virtue of the charge they carry. Because they are all negatively charged they tend to avoid one another and to keep apart. This is not at all difficult to accept in principle, even though we may be ignorant of the causes of charge repulsion. It is, however, not at all easy to estimate quantitatively the degree of correlation arising from this in any but the most simple systems.

Charge correlation is acceptable in principle to a chemist, partly because his education has accustomed him to it, and partly because he has actually seen objects with the same charge repelling one another, and those with opposite charges attracting one another. The phenomenon of spin correlation is much more difficult to accept, partly because chemists are less accustomed to it, and partly because it is impossible ever to 'see' it happening. And yet it exerts as potent an effect in molecular structure as does charge correlation. For this reason, and also because it is a particularly important feature of the attitude adopted in this book, some space will be devoted to considering it.

To begin with, some specific examples of spin correlation will be examined. The excited states of helium, for which the orbital occupation is $1s2s$, will be used. There are, of course, two states. In one the resultant spin quantum number of the system is zero and in the other it is 1. In the former case we say the spins are opposed ($-\frac{1}{2}+\frac{1}{2}=0$), and in the latter that the spins are parallel so that $S=+\frac{1}{2}+\frac{1}{2}=1$. Because the total wave function, which is, to a good approximation, the product of a spin part and a space part, must satisfy certain symmetry requirements, the nature and symmetry of the spin part affects the form of the space part. The result of this is found to be that, if the spins are parallel, the electrons tend to keep apart to a greater extent than if no symmetry requirements operated at all. On the other hand, if the resultant spin is zero ('spins opposed'), the electrons tend to come closer together than if no symmetry requirements operated. Figures 7*a* and 7*b* show, for these two states, the probability as a function of the distances of the two electrons from the nucleus. It will be seen, in the first place, that, if the spins are parallel, there is a zero probability of the two electrons being at the same radius, and moreover that the configurations of high probability are those in which one electron is close to, and the other far away from, the nucleus. On the other hand, if the spins are opposed, Fig. 7*b* shows that there is a considerable probability of both electrons being near the nucleus simultaneously. The effect of the electrons tending to separate when the spins are parallel is the reason why that state is lower in energy than the other one, for the separation of the electrons reduces inter-electron repulsion (Hund's rule).

In the two-electron system, while it is possible to say (when the resultant spin is zero) that the two electrons have opposed spins, it is not possible (because electrons cannot be distinguished) to say which electron has a spin of $+\frac{1}{2}$ and which a spin of $-\frac{1}{2}$. However this does not lead to any difficulty because, as with charges, there is no absolute significance in the + and −, but only a relative one. Consequently it is enough to know that the two electrons have opposite spins. However, the consideration of systems containing more than two electrons is markedly more complicated, because it is no longer possible to specify even which have the same and which opposite spin. Thus, if a system contained four electrons, two of each spin, it would not be possible, because of the indistinguishability of electrons, to define how the spins were distributed among the electrons. If the electrons were disposed in four separate orbitals, it would not even be possible to assign particular

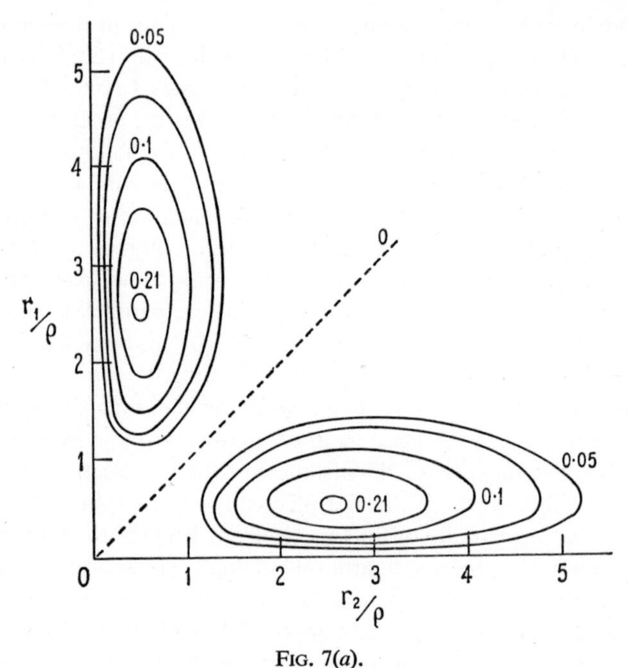

FIG. 7(*a*).

FIG. 7. Contour diagrams for helium atoms having the configuration 1*s*, 2*s* showing the probability of finding one electron at radius r_1, and the other at radius r_2 ($4\pi r_1^2 . 4\pi r_2^2 . \psi^2$). Dotted lines show zero value. The diagrams are for (*a*) the triplet, and (*b*) the singlet states (*see opposite page*).

spins to particular orbitals. This means that we do not know whether electrons 1 and 2 have the same spin or opposite spin. We just know that, if the resultant is zero, two electrons must have one spin and two the other.

Because of these difficulties, arising from our inability to distinguish electrons, we will first examine the behaviour of two to six particles which are confined to a circle. The object is to improve our experience of the effects of spin by examining a simple system. In the next few paragraphs the behaviour of particles having some, but not all of the properties of electrons will be examined. These particles will be *uncharged* but will possess *spin* in the same way as an electron. By doing this, we can examine the effects of spin on spatial distribution without these effects being obscured by those of charge. Moreover the effect can be examined

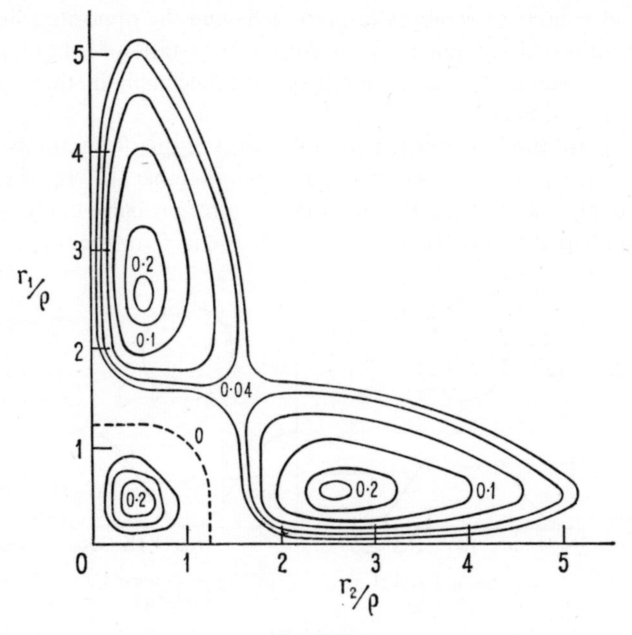

FIG. 7(*b*).

exactly because the true wave functions are available as combinations of the known single particle functions.

The states of a single particle in the system may be defined in terms of its angular momentum. This can have the values 0, +1, −1, +2, −2 ... in units of $h/2\pi$. If two particles are present and occupy the same orbital there is no correlation between their positions – they are both distributed round the circle independently of one another. That is, there is no spin correlation at all for two electrons occupying the same orbital (a pair).

If the two particles occupy the levels of quantum numbers 0 and +1 there are two possibilities; the resultant spin quantum number may be 0 (spins opposed) or 1 (spins parallel). Points on the circle may be defined by the angle ϕ, varying from 0 to 360°. The probability is a function of the angular separation of the two particles ($\Delta\phi$). If the spins are parallel this probability is proportional to $(1-\cos \Delta\phi)$; if they are opposed it is proportional to $(1+\cos \Delta\phi)$. The first of these is zero when $\Delta\phi$ is zero, and a maximum when $\Delta\phi = 180°$. The second is zero when $\Delta\phi = 180°$, and a maximum when $\Delta\phi = 0$. These results are shown graphically in Fig. 8, where there are also diagrams indicating the most probable configurations. In these diagrams a cross ($\times$) is used to represent a particle having one spin, and a circle to represent a particle having the opposite spin (○). This result is entirely similar to that for the $1s2s$ states of helium. In that case, the correlation was in–out (from the nucleus); in this, it is an angular correlation.

If there are three particles, two in the level of quantum number zero and the other in that defined by the quantum number $+1$ (the result for -1 would be the same), it is found that the most probable configuration is that in which two particles are opposite (i.e. $\Delta\phi$ for them is 180°). If

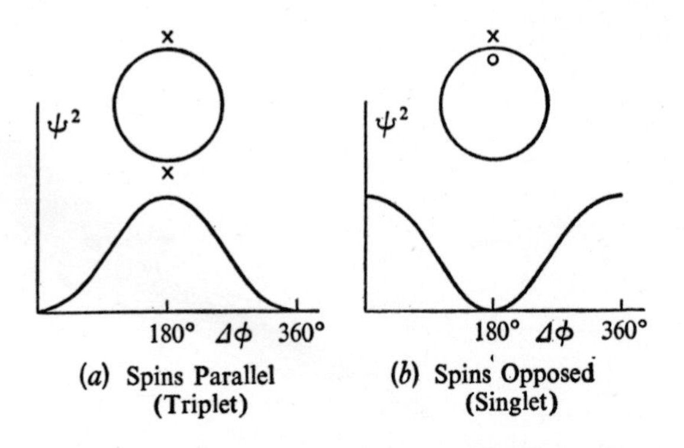

FIG. 8. Two uncharged particles on a circle with angular momentum quantum numbers 0 and 1. The graphs show the variation of ψ^2 with $\Delta\phi$ for (*a*) the triplet, and (*b*) the singlet states. The diagrams show most probable arrangements.

two particles are opposite one another, the probability is independent of the position of the third. If two particles are in the same place and the third is opposite, the two particles at the same place must have opposed spins. If the three particles are at 0°, 90° and 180°, and the resultant spin quantum number of the state is $+\frac{1}{2}$, there is a 75% chance that the particle at 0° has a spin of $+\frac{1}{2}$ and the same that the one at 180° has a spin of $+\frac{1}{2}$. The chance that the particle at 90° has a spin of $+\frac{1}{2}$ is 50%. One cannot locate the spins precisely but the configuration of highest probability is, in fact, the one we would expect if we considered two particles of the same spin keeping as far apart as possible by spin correlation, and the particle of the other spin being, in effect, uncorrelated. Moreover, this view of the system is consistent with the most probable spin distribution, in that the particles which are opposite one another tend to have the same spin. The results for this system are shown in Fig. 9.

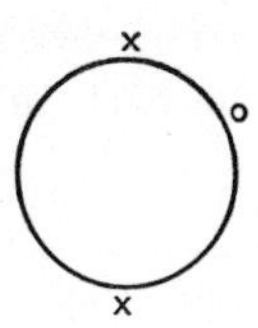

FIG. 9. The most probable disposition of three uncharged particles on a circle having angular momentum quantum numbers 0, 0 and 1. The probability is a maximum when two particles are opposite but is then independent of the position of the other particle.

If three particles are present, all having the same spin and occupying the orbitals having quantum numbers 0, +1 and −1, the most probable configuration is that in which they are equally spaced round the ring at 120° to one another. The graphs in Fig. 10 show the probability of two sets of configurations which differ from this: (*a*) one particle $\Delta\phi$ from another which is $\Delta\phi$ from the third; (*b*) two particles at 120° from one another, the third being $\Delta\phi$ from one of these and $(240-\Delta\phi)$ from the

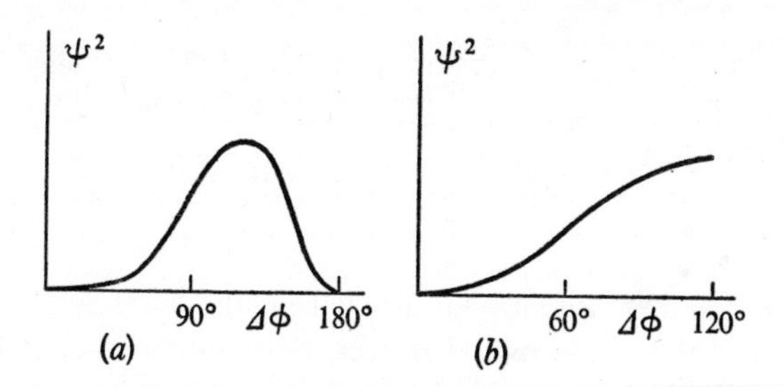

FIG. 10. Variation of ψ^2 with $\Delta\phi$ for three uncharged particles on a circle with angular momentum quantum numbers 0, +1, −1 and all having the same spin.

(*a*) Particles at ϕ, $\phi+\Delta\phi$, $\phi+2\Delta\phi$.
(*b*) Particles at ϕ, $\phi-120°$, $\phi+\Delta\phi$.

other. It will be seen that, as before, the probability is zero when two particles are at the same place and, further, that configurations in which the particles are near one another have a low relative probability.

Figure 11 shows some results for the four-electron system in which two particles occupy the orbital of quantum number zero, and two that of quantum number $+1$. Of necessity these must be two particles of each spin. The most probable configuration is that in which two particles are at the same place and two are directly opposite. The variation of probability with $\Delta\phi$, when the four particles are at $0, \Delta\phi, 180°$ and $180°+\Delta\phi$, is shown in Fig. 11. The variation with $\Delta\phi'$ when the four particles are at $0, 0, \Delta\phi'$ and $180°$ is also shown in Fig. 11. The first of these shows that, providing the particles are present in two sets, in each of which the

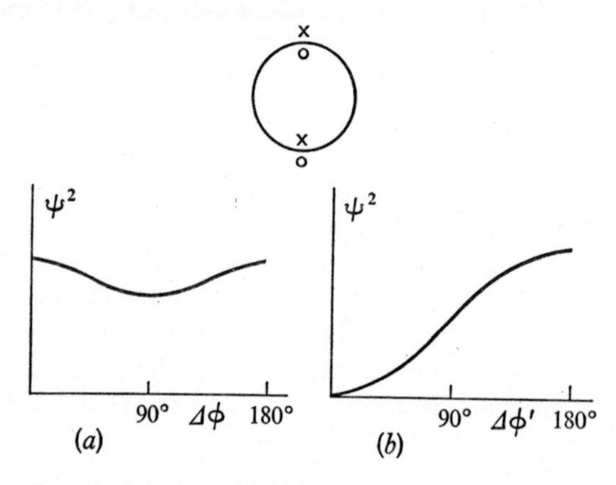

FIG. 11. Variation of ψ^2 with $\Delta\phi$ and $\Delta\phi'$ for four uncharged particles on a circle with angular momentum quantum numbers 0, 0, 1, 1.

(*a*) Particles at $0, \Delta\phi, 180°, 180°+\Delta\phi$.
(*b*) Particles at $0, 0, \Delta\phi', 180°$.

particles are opposite, the probability is near the maximum; the lowest is even 75% of the maximum. However, the results in the second graph show that, if only one particle is displaced, the probability falls very much more sharply. Again, the same qualitative result would be obtained by considering that there are two particles of one spin which tend to be opposite one another, and two of the other which also tend to be opposite one another. It may be supposed that this behaviour is governed by the tendency of particles having the same spin to keep apart. The tendency of particles of opposite spins to come together (cf. Fig. 8) provides the reason why the configuration shown in Fig. 11 is the most probable one.

The next system to be considered will be that in which there are two particles in the levels having $l=0$ and $l=+1$ and one in that having

$l = -1$. The most probable configuration is that in which there are three particles equally spaced round the ring (at 120° to one another), and the other two are opposite one another (i.e. at 180° to one another). The probability is independent of the orientation of the set of two relative to the set of three. That is, the most probable configuration is that with electrons at ϕ, $\phi + 120°$, $\phi + 240°$, ϕ' and $\phi' + 180°$, the probability being independent of both ϕ and ϕ'. This result is illustrated in Fig. 12 in which the most probable distribution of particle spin for the most probable spatial configuration is shown. This result is analogous to that for the system of three particles, two with one spin and one with the other. In both cases the distribution can be considered as the particles of each spin adopting their distribution of maximum probability, but there being no correlation between the two sets.

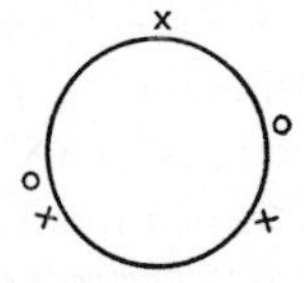

FIG. 12. Most probable arrangement of five uncharged particles having angular momentum quantum numbers 0, 0, +1, +1, −1; three at 120° to one another, two at 180° to one another.

The most probable configuration for six particles distributed as three pairs in the levels having quantum numbers 0, +1 and −1 is, as would be expected, as three equally spaced pairs (i.e. the six particles are at $\phi, \phi, \phi + 120°, \phi + 120°, \phi + 240°, \phi + 240°$). This is shown in Fig. 13 and is analogous to that of two pairs shown in Fig. 11. However, as with the two pairs, configurations in which the particles are at ϕ, $\phi + 120°$, $\phi + 240°$, ϕ', $\phi' + 120°$, $\phi' + 240°$ are not very dependent on $\phi - \phi'$. The maximum probability is with $\phi - \phi' = 0$, the minimum with $\phi - \phi' = 60°$. At the minimum the probability is 56% of that at the maximum.

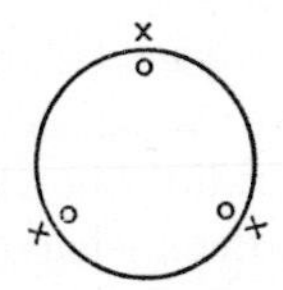

FIG. 13. Most probable arrangement of six uncharged particles having angular momentum quantum numbers 0, 0, +1, +1, −1, −1.

The general conclusion from these simple examples, therefore, is that it is satisfactory, for a qualitative picture, to think of the particles in two sets, one set being made up of particles of one spin and the other of the other spin. The most probable disposition of the particles is that in which the particles of each set adopt the most probable disposition for that set (opposite for 2, equilateral triangular for 3). If there are equal numbers of particles in each set, then the most probable configuration is that in which the particles are placed as pairs. If there are unequal numbers in each set, then the probability is independent of the mutual disposition of the two sets.

In the following pages of this book there will be references back to this section both directly and indirectly; some of these references will be specified and some not. The atomic and molecular systems under consideration contain electrons which differ from the above particles in being charged. Because all have the same charge, all repel one another. Therefore, for sets of electrons which have the same spin, the effects of charge correlation will add to the effects of spin correlation, and thus the tendency of electrons with parallel spin to keep apart will be enhanced. That is, the tendency of two such electrons to be opposite one another will be greater, as also will the tendency of three electrons to be disposed as an equilateral triangle. The effect of charge correlation, however, will operate against the effects of spin correlation for those particles which have opposed spins. For instance, for the six-particle system dealt with above, the effect of charge correlation will be to reduce the probability of the electrons being disposed as pairs and to increase the probability of their being disposed at intervals of 60° round the ring. The combination of these two effects is therefore likely to mean that there is probably very little correlation between electrons of opposed spin. On the other hand, for electrons of parallel spin, the correlation effect is likely to be very high.

1.7 Electron Correlation in Neon and Related Ions

The spatial correlation of the eight electrons in the filled shell of quantum number 2 has important consequences for chemists. The considerations of the last section suggest that, in neon, for configurations in which the eight electrons are approximately equidistant from the nucleus, four of the electrons (which may be thought of as having parallel spins since there is a high probability of this being so) will have a high tendency to be disposed at the corners of a regular tetrahedron, and the other four (which have a high probability of having spins opposite to those of the first set) will also tend to be situated at the corners of a regular tetrahedron. Correlation within each of these tetrahedra will be strong because of the cooperative effects of charge and spin correlation, and any displacement of an electron or electrons away from the disposition will result in a sharp drop in probability. On the other hand, the correlation between the two tetrahedral sets is not expected to be *strong* because of the *opposing* effects of charge and spin correlation. However, if there are other effects, such as the disposition of nearby charges, it may be expected that the two sets will be drawn together, providing that this leads to a lowering in the potential energy of the system (despite inter-electron repulsion). On the other hand, if no such potential advantage exists, then the two tetrahedral sets will probably not be coincident, so that the de-stabilizing effects of inter-electron repulsion will be reduced. There may be intermediate cases. For instance, it would be possible for the disposition of the electrons to be such that one corner of each tetrahedron was coincident (or near-coincident) while the other three were not. This might happen when a proton approaches a fluoride ion. In this case two electrons would be drawn towards the proton, despite their mutual repulsion, but the other six would keep apart, to reduce inter-electron repulsion, while still maintaining the two tetrahedral sets.

It must, in all honesty, be stressed at this stage that there is no *proof* that this is the correct way to regard the electron octet in the second quantum shell. However, the general considerations about spin presented in the last section, together with simple ideas regarding the effect of charge, suggest that such an attitude or hypothesis might be successful. The remainder of this book will be devoted almost entirely to applying the ideas contained in this section and the last one to the structure of molecules and to chemical problems which are dependent on structure. The attitude finally adopted to this approach to the qualitative discussion of electron distribution must depend therefore on the achievements of the following chapters.

CHAPTER TWO

Chemical Binding

2.1 Introduction

In this chapter the means by which elements combine together to form compounds will be considered. In the first place the ideas of G. N. Lewis regarding ionic and covalent compounds will be described. With covalent compounds, they will be presented on the basis of the suggestions advanced at the end of the last chapter. Various examples will be used and in particular the chemical bond in the hydrogen molecule ion, H_2^+, and the hydrogen molecule, H_2, will be examined.

2.2 Types of Chemical Binding

The properties of chemical substances show that they can be divided into two types. These are called ionic and covalent. Ionic compounds, which are soluble in water, give solutions which conduct electricity in a manner which shows that charged particles of atomic and molecular size are present (called ions). Others, which are not soluble in water, will conduct when melted. These, and others which will not dissolve and cannot be melted, are shown by examination by X-ray diffraction to consist, in the solid state, of closely packed arrangements of oppositely charged ions held together by electrostatic forces. Examples of ionic compounds are sodium chloride, calcium fluoride, magnesium bromide and lithium oxide. Covalent compounds do not usually give conducting solutions, and the properties of their crystals, such as a relatively low melting point, show that the separate particles making up the solid are uncharged and therefore much less tightly bound to one another. Examples are methane, ethyl alcohol, benzene, carbon tetrachloride, sulphur hexafluoride, chlorine monoxide, and phosphorus tribromide. There are examples of ionic compounds in which one or both of the ions consists of a collection of atoms held together in the manner of the molecules of covalent compounds. Examples are ammonium chloride, $NH_4^+Cl^-$; sodium nitrate, $Na^+NO_3^-$; potassium sulphate, $K_2^+SO_4^=$; ammonium acetate, $NH_4^+CH_3COO^-$.

2.3 Ionic Compounds

It was shown in section 1.5, that the lithium atom has the electronic structure $1s^2 2s$. The electron in the $2s$ orbital is under the influence of a field which is a resultant of that due to the nucleus of charge $+3$ and the two electrons in the $1s$ orbital. Because the behaviour of this group of particles is similar to that of a nucleus carrying a charge of about $+1\frac{1}{2}$, and because the electron is in a level having $n = 2$, it is not too difficult to remove. It needs about 124 kcal/g atom. To remove a further electron would require much more energy (1730 kcal/g atom) because the quantum number of the orbital occupied by the second electron is 1, and because the effective charge of the nucleus is now nearly $+3$. Consequently, one electron is easily lost but not a second. For sodium a similar situation exists but the energy to remove one electron is less (118 kcal/g atom), because the principal quantum number of the orbital involved is 3. The removal of a second electron is energetically prohibitive (1088 kcal/g atom). For potassium it requires 100 kcal/g atom to remove the first electron, and 733 kcal/g atom to remove the second.

For beryllium, the first and second electrons are fairly easy to remove, requiring 215 kcal/g atom and 420 kcal/g atom respectively, while the third is very much more difficult (3540 kcal/g atom) because an electron from a $1s$ orbital is involved. The energy to remove the second electron is greater than that to remove the first because the second electron is being abstracted from a system which already carries one positive charge. The high energy necessary to remove the second electron is one reason why ionic compounds containing Be^{++} are uncommon. For magnesium the energies to remove the first, second and third electrons are 176, 346, and 1845 kcal/g atom respectively. The smaller value of the second means that it is easier to form Mg^{++} than to form Be^{++}. The three energies for calcium are 141, 273 and 1180 kcal/g atom.

The above figures show that it is *relatively* easy to remove electrons from the atoms of Li, Na, K, Be, Mg and Ca to produce ions which have the electronic structure of the atoms of He, Ne and A respectively. This is one of the examples of the attainment of the inert gas structure. However, it should be remembered *at all times* that this rule is only important because it serves as a useful guide to the energy changes attending the loss of electrons.

The fluorine atom has the electronic structure $1s^2 2s^2 2p^5$. An electron in a p orbital experiences from the neighbourhood of the nucleus a field approximating to that which would be produced by a charge of $+5$ (the nuclear charge less the effect of the four electrons in the 1*s* and 2*s* orbitals). It also experiences the repulsion of the other electrons in the 2*p* orbitals, but some of these are on the other side of the atom, and so do not balance out an equal charge on the nucleus. As a result, the energy to remove an electron is quite high (402 kcal/g atom), and F^+ cannot be formed by an ordinary chemical process, since, for such processes, the energy available is much less. However, the fluorine atom can take up another electron to give F^- and this process ($F+e \rightarrow F^-$) evolves 84 kcal/g atom. The reason for this is that the fluorine atom can accommodate an electron in a 2*p* orbital, and this does not suffer a repulsion from the other five electrons in 2*p* orbitals sufficient to outweigh the attraction of a central positive charge of effectively +5. A chlorine atom

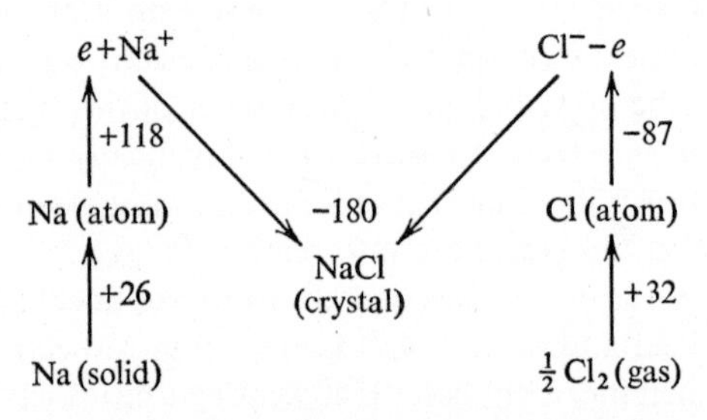

FIG. 14. Diagram showing the thermochemistry of formation of NaCl (crystal) from $Na+\frac{1}{2}Cl_2$. The figures are in kcal/g atom.

also has a positive electron affinity amounting to 87 kcal/g atom. For bromine the figure is 82 kcal/g atom.

The reason why ionic compounds are formed, therefore, may be illustrated using the formation of sodium chloride from sodium and chlorine as an example. The sodium must first be vaporized to atoms (requiring 26 kcal/g atom); the chlorine molecule must be dissociated to give atoms (requiring 32 kcal/g atom); the sodium atom must be ionized to give Na^+ plus an electron (requiring 118 kcal/g atom) and this electron must be added to a chlorine atom yielding 87 kcal/g atom. The above processes have required 89 kcal/g mol. The electrostatic energy resulting from the assembly of the positive and negative ions into a crystal (180 kcal/g mol) more than provides this energy, so that sodium and chlorine react together to give an ionic crystal. The sequence is shown diagrammatically in Fig. 14. Similar arguments apply to all the alkali metal halides.

However, suppose we consider qualitatively the possibility of forming $NaCl_2$, containing Na^{++}. The production of Na^{++} will require an extra 1088 kcal/g atom. For this to happen the source of energy would have to be the additional electrostatic energy for the assembly of the double positive ions with the chloride ions in a crystal. While this would give much more energy, calculations by Grimm and Herzfeld have shown that it would not be enough (*Z. Phys.*, 1923). Consequently $NaCl_2$ is not formed, but only NaCl. The satisfactory rule is, therefore, the attainment of the inert gas structure by Na in Na^+. This provides a correct guide to the electronic structure at which the further removal of an electron will be prohibitive energetically.

Sodium chloride also exists as separate ions in aqueous solutions; again, as with the crystal, we may imagine the production of gaseous sodium and chloride ions at the expenditure of 89 kcal/g mol. In this case the energy is recovered by the solvation of the ions in the solution. That is, the energy is recovered as the electrostatic energy gained by orienting the dipolar water molecules; the positive part of those near the negative ion are directed towards it, and the negative part (the oxygen) of those near the positive sodium ion are directed towards it. The solvation energy of Na^{++} would be greater than that of Na^+, because of its larger charge, but this increase would be insufficient to provide the very large amount of energy required to give Na^{++} from Na^+.

With magnesium and chlorine (or any halogen) the situation is different. As with sodium and chlorine it would require energy to produce $Mg^+ + Cl^-$, and this would be more than recovered by the electrostatic energy released on the formation of the close assembly of ions in crystalline MgCl. However, in this case, because the energy to produce Mg^{++} from Mg^+ (346) is not as great as that to produce Na^{++} from Na^+ (1088), the gain in lattice energy obtained with doubly charged cations will outweigh the energy expended in the production of Mg^{++}. Consequently $MgCl_2$ will be more stable than MgCl. In this case the energy to produce Mg^{3+} (1845) is prohibitive, because it far outweighs the additional energy that would be obtained by incorporating triply positively charged ions in the lattice. Similar arguments would apply to the stability of aqueous solutions of $MgCl_2$ relative to those of MgCl and $MgCl_3$. Again, the rule regarding the attainment of the inert gas structure provides a satisfactory guide to defining which particular ion will be the stable one, and what valency the metal will have.

The elements oxygen, sulphur and selenium have two electrons less than the next inert gas. In the ions $O^=$, $S^=$ and $Se^=$ these atoms also attain the inert gas structure. However, the position here is a little different from that for the halogens, and therefore deserves special mention. Oxygen will be used as the example. An isolated atom of oxygen can take up an electron to give O^- and energy is evolved to the extent of approximately 40 kcal/g atom. However, the *isolated* oxygen ion O^- cannot take up another electron because of the presence already of a negative charge on the O^-. It is estimated that it would require 210 kcal/g atom to force an electron into the remaining available $2p$ orbital of O^-. This means that the overall process of formation of an $O^=$ ion from an O atom is endothermic to the extent of about 170 kcal/g atom. Why then is it satisfactory to regard lithium oxide, Li_2O, and magnesium oxide, MgO, as ionic solids? The reason is, of course, that the very large lattice energies, arising from the assembly of the positive ions and *doubly* charged negative ions into a lattice, is sufficiently great to provide the energy, not only to ionize the positive ion, but also to produce the doubly charged oxygen ions. Put in another way: while O^- in isolation cannot take up another electron, an O^- ion surrounded by eight positively charged lithium ions, or six doubly positively charged magnesium ions can take up an electron, because of the electrostatic potential produced by this array of positive charges.

If the fluoride ion, F^-, or the oxygen ion, $O^=$, were to take up another electron it would have to be accommodated in a $3s$ orbital, that is, in the next quantum shell. Having regard to the electrostatic repulsion existing between the negative ion and the approaching electron, this is not possible. Moreover it is impossible by any array of positive charges to make it worth while energetically. Consequently $F^=$ and O^{3-} do not exist, and again the attainment of the inert gas structure provides a satisfactory rule for the number of electrons that will be taken up, and hence for the valency of these non-metallic elements.

The purpose of this section has been to show why the 'attainment of the inert gas structure' is a good rule to use, and the way in which energy considerations account for its success. It must be stressed that these energy considerations are what matters, and that the rule must only be applied in a sensible way where it is applicable. For instance it does not apply to the formation of ions such as Mn^{++} and Fe^{+++} but the general energy considerations of this section can be used to explain why ionic compounds involving these ions do exist and are stable. Nevertheless, for atoms having atomic numbers near those of the inert gases, the rule is a most valuable and successful one. It includes all elements in the first and second periods (the short periods) and those at the beginning and end of the long periods (e.g. K, Ca, Sc, Se and Br in the third period).

2.4 Covalent Binding

It is clear that the binding of two hydrogen atoms (2H) together to form a hydrogen molecule (H_2) is quite different from the relatively simple electrostatic forces that hold the sodium and chloride ions together in a crystalline lattice. For instance, two similar atoms are held together whereas ionic compounds require, of necessity, the participation of opposites. Secondly, the absence of conductivity under all conditions (solid, liquid, gas or solution) shows that separate charged particles are not involved. For a long time this binding has been represented by H—H, the line being said to represent a *chemical bond.* Since the discovery of electrons and the increased understanding of their participation in the structure of atoms, it has been realized that this chemical bond is made up of electrons and can only be understood in terms of the behaviour of electrons. About fifty years ago G. N. Lewis identified it with two electrons, usually referred to as a 'shared pair of electrons'. This proposal is probably the most important and productive contribution that has ever been made to the subject of valency and chemical binding (*J.A.C.S.*, 1916).

A hydrogen atom has one electron in the 1*s* orbital. This orbital can accommodate another electron providing the spins of the two electrons are opposed. As a consequence, the hydrogen atom has a small electron affinity, and the gas-phase process $H + e \rightarrow H^-$ is accompanied by the evolution of 16 kcal/g atom. The smallness of this makes H^- a very unstable species, which is only encountered in ionic lattices in which a strong field can be maintained at the location of H^-. For example, it exists in lithium hydride because a number of small Li^+ ions can be brought close to the H^-. However, another possibility exists. If two hydrogen atoms are brought together, and the two electrons have opposed spins, each atom is capable of accommodating the electron of the other into its 1*s* orbital. As a consequence, the electron on one atom in the bi-nuclear system is drawn to a small extent into the 1*s* orbital of the other and, of course, vice versa. The system may be considered as having the following electron distribution: one electron distributed in an orbital which is roughly $(1s_A + \frac{1}{8}1s_B)$, and the other in an orbital which is roughly $(1s_B + \frac{1}{8}1s_A)$. Because of our inability to distinguish between electrons it is not possible to say which electron is in which orbital, and in the wave function necessary for quantum mechanical calculations the two dispositions must be given equal weight. As a consequence of the presence of the other nucleus, the electrons on each atom are drawn slightly into the region between the nuclei, and the probability of finding one or other of them there is enhanced. This results in a lowering of the potential and total energy of the system, and produces a binding between the two atoms. This type of binding can occur if there is an orbital on the atom A available for occupation by the electron provided by atom B, and vice versa. Consider two hydrogen atoms coming together in such a way that the electron spins are parallel. Then atom A does not have an orbital available for the electron on B, because they cannot both occupy the $1s$ orbital on atom A. Consequently the slight drift of the electron into the nuclear region is prohibited by the effect of the Pauli Exclusion Principle, which operates to keep the electrons apart and out of the internuclear region. Hence two hydrogen atoms, in which the electron spins are parallel, do not attract one another.

If two helium atoms approach one another, the fact that the $1s$ orbitals on both atoms are filled means that there is no suitable orbital on B for an electron on A to move into, nor vice versa. Consequently no chemical bond is formed and, except for a weak van der Waals (polarization) attraction at large distances, the two atoms repel one another.

From the above it is apparent that if two atoms, A and B, each of which has an orbital containing one electron, are brought together then, if the orbital energies are approximately equal, a pair-bond will be formed providing the electron spins are opposed. The bond, consisting of two electrons, is formed because, for each electron, the availability of an orbital on the other atom means that the probability of the electrons being between the positive nuclei is enhanced, and this provides binding. It is impossible to determine the detailed dynamics of the electrons in such systems except in a very few cases. This difficulty of solving the Schrödinger equation for systems containing two or more electrons means that the development of the electron-pair bond has to be based, to a large extent, on empirical reasoning.

2.5 Other Covalent Compounds

Consider the formation of HF by a hydrogen atom and a fluorine atom. The electronic structures are respectively $1s$ and $1s^2 2s^2 2p^5$, so that each atom has a vacant orbital capable of taking in an electron. Consequently, if the spin of the electron on the hydrogen atom is opposed to that occupying the half-filled orbital on the fluorine, an electron-pair covalent bond can be formed by the same type of mechanism as for H_2. Thus a molecule, which can be written as H—F, is formed. In the molecule neither the H nor the F has now a low-lying vacant orbital and, consequently, no further bonds can be formed by HF and it is therefore a saturated and stable molecule.

It is apparent that the rule stating that atomic systems tend to attain the electronic structure of an inert gas molecule is again a useful one. The two electrons may be regarded as being shared between the 1*s* orbital of the hydrogen and one of the 2*p* orbitals of the fluorine. Counting the shared pair into the electronic systems of *both* atoms, the hydrogen has the electron content of helium and the fluorine the electron content of neon. The reason that they have no further orbitals suitable for forming another bond is because all the orbitals of the particular principal quantum number have been fully used (as in the inert gas).

Fluorine atoms can combine together to give F_2 by sharing a pair between them. There is a vacancy in one of the 2*p* orbitals on each atom and, providing the spins of the electrons are opposed, each is capable of accommodating the electron of the other, and a pair bond is formed. Each fluorine atom may be regarded as having attained the electron content of neon by sharing. The molecule is written as F—F. The molecules HF and F_2 may be represented, in the manner of G. N. Lewis, by

$$\mathrm{H}:\overset{\cdot\cdot}{\underset{\cdot\cdot}{\mathrm{F}}}: \quad \text{and} \quad :\overset{\cdot\cdot}{\underset{\cdot\cdot}{\mathrm{F}}}:\overset{\cdot\cdot}{\underset{\cdot\cdot}{\mathrm{F}}}:.$$

Each dot represents an electron (the two 1*s* electrons on the fluorine atom are omitted). This is a most successful diagrammatic way of representing the attainment of the inert-gas structure and, therefore, in the case of fluorine, the completion of the octet (i.e. the octet of electrons in the valence shell which has a quantum number 2).

The molecules of water and of ammonia may be represented by

$$\begin{array}{c} :\overset{\cdot\cdot}{\underset{\cdot\cdot}{\mathrm{O}}}:\mathrm{H} \\ \mathrm{H}\phantom{:\mathrm{H}} \end{array} \quad \text{and} \quad \begin{array}{c} \mathrm{H}:\overset{\cdot\cdot}{\underset{\cdot\cdot}{\mathrm{N}}}:\mathrm{H} \\ \mathrm{H} \end{array}.$$

In the oxygen atom two 2*p* orbitals are half-filled (see Table 1, page 10) and so, by the mechanism described in some detail for H_2, bonds can be formed to two hydrogen atoms. With ammonia the situation is similar, only three bonds can be formed, because the nitrogen has three electrons fewer than neon, which means that there are three $2p$ orbitals containing only one electron each. Consequently the electrons from three hydrogen atoms can be absorbed, and NH_3 is formed.

The carbon atom in its ground state has the electronic structure $1s^2 2s^2 2p_{+1} 2p_0$. It would therefore be expected to be divalent since there are two half-filled $2p$ orbitals. It is, of course, quadrivalent. This may be explained by considering the process as a somewhat idealized sequence of events. The carbon atom is excited by transferring one of the $2s$ electrons to the third $2p$ orbital giving $1s^2 2s 2p_{+1} 2p_0 2p_{-1}$. There are now four half-filled orbitals and consequently four electron-pair bonds can be formed as depicted by

```
    H
    ••
H : C : H
    ••
    H
```
.

The four shared pairs then give the carbon atom an octet of electrons and the electron content of the neon atom. The formation of the two extra bonds makes the expenditure of energy on excitation of the carbon atom worthwhile.

In section 1.7 it was concluded that the octet of electrons in the outer shell of neon was best regarded as two spin-sets of four, the electrons in each set being disposed, in the most probable configuration, at the corners of a tetrahedron. The two tetrahedra were thought to be loosely correlated to one another, because of the opposing effects of charge and spin correlation in this particular case. In the methane molecule, the two tetrahedra will tend to be disposed so that both sets place electrons with high probability in the regions near the protons, where the potential energy is low. Therefore the two tetrahedra will be oriented similarly, despite the adverse effects of inter-electron repulsion, because this is outweighed by the effects of the positive protons. Consequently the protons are held in the form of a tetrahedron by electron pairs. In this case it is immaterial whether the octet is regarded as two tetrahedra of electrons, or four pairs. The approach contained in this book would favour the double-tetrahedra viewpoint but, on the other hand, it must be remembered that the Pauli Principle places the limitation that only two electrons can occupy the same region of space with the same momentum, and then only if their spins are opposed.

In ammonia, the most effective way energetically to bind the three protons is to dispose the two tetrahedral quartets of electrons in near proximity, so that there are pairs of electrons to bind the three protons. Again the descriptions in terms of two tetrahedral sets or four pairs are, in effect, identical. The HNH angle is 107° which is close to the regular tetrahedral angle ($109\frac{1}{2}$) in CH_4. In ammonia there are, therefore, three shared-pairs and one lone-pair. The decrease in angle can be explained in terms of the protons distorting slightly the regular tetrahedral distribution. The situation is similar in H_2O, where again the two tetrahedra must be similarly disposed to bind simultaneously the two protons, and therefore the electrons are arranged as two shared- and two lone-pairs. The HOH angle is $104\frac{1}{2}$° which is still close to the tetrahedral angle.

In HF, there is one shared-pair. In this case, however, the two tetrahedral quartets need not be disposed similarly. One electron of each quartet must be in the region between the proton and the fluorine nucleus. However, the other three of one quartet may be staggered (round the continuation of the HF axis) relative to the three of the other quartet. This will keep the unshared electrons apart and reduce inter-electron repulsion. On this hypothesis, therefore, there is only one spatially-close electron-pair namely that in the H—F bond. The same situation will obtain in F—F, in which the only close pair will be that in the bond. All the others can keep apart and still remain members of tetrahedral distributions (see later).

All the above structures are of the type proposed by Lewis who, of course, stressed the pair, and not the tetrahedral spin-sets for the existence of electron spin, and the effects it produced were not suggested until ten years after Lewis's famous paper in the *Journal of the American Chemical Society*. Many other examples can be given, particularly from among aliphatic compounds. A few Lewis-type formulae are given below for NF_3, $(CH_3)_2S$, HOCl, and C_2H_5OH and the reader could provide many others.

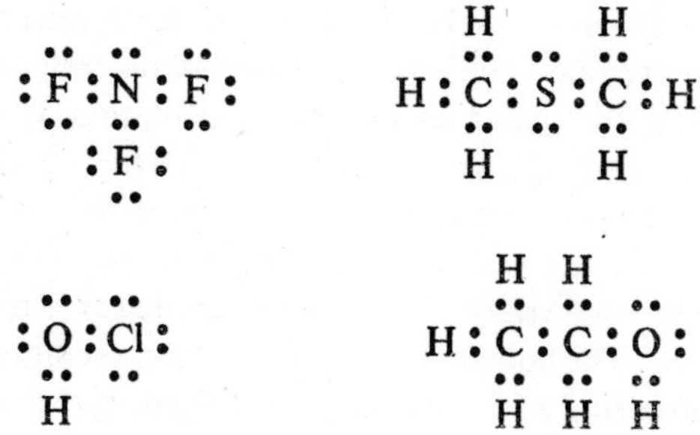

```
 ••  ••  ••              H     H
:F : N : F:              ••  ••  ••
 ••  ••  ••           H : C : S : C : H
   : F :                 ••  ••  ••
     ••                  H     H

                           H   H
 ••  ••                    ••  ••  ••
:O : Cl:                H : C : C : O :
 ••  ••                    ••  ••  ••
 H                         H   H   H
```

The treatment of double bonds and of molecules for which one single Lewis structure is not adequate will be dealt with later.

2.6 The Hydrogen Molecule and Molecule Ion

In section 2.4 the covalent bond consisting of a pair of electrons was discussed, the hydrogen molecule being used as an example. While a detailed examination of the situation would necessitate a consideration of the extent of the electron cloud, of the changes in the kinetic energy of the electrons as well as of the changes in their potential energy, the most important feature is the enhancement of electron probability in the region between the nuclei. This results in a lowering of the mean electronic potential energy, and of the total energy, and serves to bind the nuclei together. It is important to realize that this energy change is not one of some special kind arising because of the pairing of electron spins. The attitude should rather be that the Pauli Principle allows this concentration of two electrons in the internuclear region, providing the resultant spin of the two participating electrons is zero. This will be considered again after a discussion of the one-electron bond in H_2^+.

The dissociation energy of H_2^+ is 54 kcal/g mol while that of H_2 is 109. Both of these figures are obtained by observing the spectrum of hydrogen in a discharge tube, the pressure being rather higher than that used when the spectrum of atomic hydrogen is required. Too much stress should not be laid on the fact that the one-electron bond has a dissociation energy approximately half that of the two-electron bond, though the obvious similarity of the two ratios is rather tempting. What is much more important is that the dissociation energy of H_2^+ is comparable in magnitude to that of H_2, but less. The equilibrium internuclear distance of H_2^+ is 1·06 Å; that in H_2 0·74 Å. Let us consider the relative energies of the two systems in the neighbourhood of 0·75 to 1·1 Å. At this distance the internuclear repulsion is of the order of 500 kcal/g mol and is, of course, equal for H_2^+ and H_2. The lowering of electronic energy relative to that of 2H for H_2 and H and H^+ for H_2^+ at infinite separation is somewhat greater than this (binding occurs). Calculation shows (Hopton and Linnett, *J.C.S.*, 1962; Bowen and Linnett, *J.C.S.*, 1963) that the lowering in the electronic energy for H_2^+ is about 90% of that for H_2. This 10% difference accounts for the 50% difference in dissociation energy, i.e. in the total energy when the internuclear repulsion energy has been included. The conclusion suggested by these figures is that, in H_2^+, there is a lowering of electronic potential energy as a result of an enhancement of the electron probability in the region between the nuclei. As a result, there is a chemical bond in H_2^+ which may be described as a *one-electron bond.* In H_2, when the resultant electronic spin is zero, the Pauli Principle allows the second electron into the internuclear region. However, the electrostatic repulsion between the two electrons prevents the concentration of electron density being anything like twice that for one electron. Therefore the lowering of electronic energy for two electrons is only a little greater than for one. However, this is enough to make the dissociation energy of H_2 considerably greater than that of H_2^+; in fact, about twice as much. This is the reason why, in so many circumstances comparable to this, the electron-pair bond is more important than the one-electron bond. As regards the lowering of electronic energy it is a little better; as regards the lowering of the total energy it is, in relative terms, a good deal better.

The bonding energy in covalent bonds, such as those in H_2^+ and H_2, can be discussed in terms of the changes in nuclear repulsion energy, electronic potential and electronic kinetic energy. In this respect there is no new type of energy in either the one-electron or the two-electron bond. Nevertheless the calculation of this energy is extremely difficult. It is only since the advent of quantum mechanics that the proper equations have been available. Moreover it is only for H_2^+ that this fundamental equation of quantum mechanics, the Schrödinger equation, can be exactly solved, though that for H_2 can be obtained almost exactly now that high-speed computers are available. The equation cannot be solved completely to give an analytical solution when more than one electron is present, and, when there are more than two or three in the whole system, even nearly exact solutions become very difficult. Consequently there is still a great field here for the semi-empirical development of ideas regarding the structure and properties of the chemical bond.

The system of two helium atoms has already been discussed. It was shown in section 2.4 that, because of the Pauli Exclusion Principle, and the fact that the two helium atoms had filled shells (no vacant low-lying orbitals), there could be no sharing of electrons and therefore no enhancement of the electron probability in the internuclear region. The situation for $He + He^+$ (i.e. He_2^+) containing three electrons will, however, be different. The system can be envisaged as consisting of two electrons, having the same spin, occupying $1s$ orbitals on the two atoms, while the electron of the other spin is shared between the $1s$ orbitals on the two atoms. Because of the overlap of the two orbitals in the region between the helium nuclei this will result in an attraction, and a bond will be formed. The electronic structure of the molecular ion may be represented by

$$\overset{\bullet}{\mathrm{He}}\bullet\overset{\bullet}{\mathrm{He}} \quad \text{or} \quad \overset{\times}{\mathrm{He}}\circ\overset{\times}{\mathrm{He}}$$

where, as for the particles on a ring (see section 1.4), a cross is used to represent an electron of one spin, and a circle an electron of the other spin. The second formula shows that each helium atom has, associated with it, one electron of each spin, and therefore the Pauli Principle is satisfied. This principle, as can be seen, operates to prevent the other two electrons participating in bonding by keeping them apart and located on separate atoms. The dissociation energy of He_2^+ is about 70 kcal/g mol and the equilibrium bond length is 1·08 Å. Pauling has described this bond in He_2^+ as 'a three-electron bond'. This is surely an unfortunate description because, just as in H_2^+, there is essentially one electron holding the two He^+ together. The dissociation energy and internuclear distance are consistent with this conclusion. Consequently, in the remainder of this book, bonds of this type will be referred to as one-electron bonds. The term three-electron bond will be used when there *are* three electrons holding the two centres together. This phrase must not therefore be confused with Pauling's phrase. Such three-electron bonds, in the sense used here, will have bond dissociation energies greater than ordinary single (i.e. two-electron) bonds. This phraseology seems to be more internally consistent and informative.

2.7 Summary

The object of this chapter has been to consider the main factors operating in the formation of ionic and covalent compounds. With the former, consideration has to be given to the opposing energy factors of ion production and lattice formation (if the solid compound is considered). The electrostatic energy of the assembly of ions in the crystal must outweigh the energy needed for their production. Because the rule of attaining the inert gas structure provides a good guide for maintaining the energy of ion production within practicable limits, it provides a useful guide for what ions will be formed. For elements in the first short period particularly, and for the second short period also, this rule is equivalent to that which refers to the completion of the octet of electrons in the valency shell. In covalent compounds, so-called chemical bonds are formed. In these the position ions are held *together* by the concentration of electronic charge between them. Again it was found that the above rules provided correct guides as to bonds and compounds that could and would be formed as a stable system. However, in this section, it was stressed that single electrons could provide a bond of strength comparable to that of one consisting of a shared pair of electrons. The electron-pair bond is of particular importance because it is stronger than a one-electron bond, and also because the behaviour of electrons summarized by the Pauli Principle prevents three electrons occupying the same region of space at the same time. Consequently the three-electron system in He_2^+ produces a one-electron bond, so that both the one-electron and three-electron systems produce bonds which are weaker than the electron-pair bond. The wide prevalence of this type of bond is therefore understandable, but it will be shown that there are circumstances in which one-electron bonds are preferred. For instance two one-electron bonds may be preferred energetically to one electron-pair bond because thereby inter-electron repulsion energy is reduced.

CHAPTER THREE

Diatomic Molecules and Ions

3.1 Introduction

In this chapter the electronic structures of the covalently bound diatomic molecules will be discussed, together with ions such as O_2^-, CN^- and NO^+. It will be found that there are advantages in formulating the bonds in some of these species as consisting of an odd number of electrons, and not just in terms of electron pairs.

The main theme of this chapter, as of the whole book, is that the local disposition of electrons round each nucleus is very firmly controlled by the operation of the Pauli Principle and of inter-electron repulsion. Moreover it is assumed that the local situation round each atom provides a very good starting point, in most cases, for developing a description of electronic structure. In this respect this approach is basically similar to the method proposed by G. N. Lewis which became, in its quantum mechanical form, the valence-bond method. It is, in this sense, opposite to the molecular orbital method which takes the view that particular attention to the local situation is less important than the proper incorporation into the treatment of the full symmetry of the whole molecule. The two methods may therefore be said to provide opposite approaches to the problem of the electronic structure of molecules. This statement is not intended to mean that one is right and one wrong. Though the method used here is essentially similar, as regards its starting point, to the valence bond method, it differs from it in an important respect. Whereas the G. N. Lewis method gives to the neighbourhood of each atom, in the First Short Period, an octet of electrons made up of four pairs, the approach presented here gives to each an octet made up of two spin-sets of four, each set of four having a strong tendency to be tetrahedrally disposed. In some circumstances, the two tetrahedral sets are disposed essentially as four pairs (e.g. CH_4, NH_3 and H_2O, see section 2.5). But, in other cases, the two tetrahedra may not be similarly oriented. Such a distribution possesses the energetic advantage of reducing inter-electron repulsion and, if no other overriding disadvantages are involved, this advantage will prove decisive. For a long time great stress has been paid to the 'pairing' of electrons. This has produced, in the minds of many chemists, an idea that there is some special effect arising from the pairing of electrons which lowers the energy. In these terms such an idea is totally mistaken. It appears even that, in certain circumstances, the association of electrons in spatial pairs is a disadvantage (if, for instance, an equal level of bonding can be achieved without pairing; see later). The reason pairs *are* important is that the Pauli Principle permits them; that is, it permits two electrons to occupy the same spatial region if they have opposed spins, and, in many molecules, the greatest binding (reduction in the potential energy) can be achieved by disposing of the electrons in pairs. This situation has already been encountered in NH_3 and H_2O.

3.2 Fluorine and Oxygen Diatomic Molecules

The electronic structure of fluorine has been described earlier as

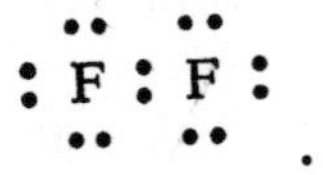

```
  ••  ••
: F : F :
  ••  ••  .
```

This might also be depicted by

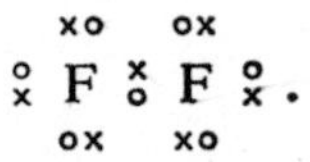

```
  xo   ox
° F ˣ F °
x   °   x .
  ox   xo
```

In this case the seven electrons of one spin are expected to be distributed at the corners of two tetrahedra with one common apex which is situated on the line joining the two nuclei. The nuclei are at the centres of the tetrahedra, which can have any relative orientation about the FF axis with respect to one another. The electrons of the other spin are at the corners of two other tetrahedra which also have a common apex on the internuclear axis (see Fig. 15). There must therefore be two electrons, as a pair, between the nuclei. However, there need be no other spatial paris because, except for the coincident apex between the nuclei, the two separate tetrahedral spin-sets round *one* nucleus can be staggered relative to one another, and this will tend to keep the electrons apart. It can be said that there are no lone-*pairs*, if that term is used to mean a pair occupying the same spatial orbital. The six unshared electrons in each atom will be disposed separately from one another, but the pair in the internuclear region will occupy the same orbital and be close to one another; the two bonding electrons *can* be regarded as a spatial 'pair'.

The equilibrium bond length for the oxygen molecule in its ground electronic state is 1·21 Å. That in HO—OH is 1·48 Å (see Appendix). Since the latter molecule must contain an electron-pair bond the shortness of the bond in O_2 suggests that the binding is tighter and that more

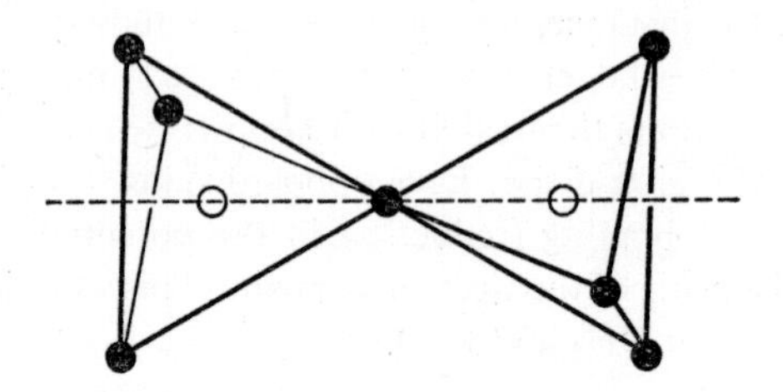

FIG. 15. Diagram of seven electrons arranged as two tetrahedra having a common apex between the two nuclei which are shown as circles in the centre of each tetrahedron.

electrons must be involved. An oxygen atom has the electronic structure $1s^2 2s^2 2p^4$. There are two $2p$ orbitals which are only half-filled, and can therefore accept electrons. This suggests that two pair-bonds might be formed between the oxygen atoms, the structure being

$$\overset{+\circ}{\underset{\circ+}{}}\text{O}\ \begin{smallmatrix}\times\\ \circ\\ \times\\ \circ\end{smallmatrix}\ \text{O}\overset{\circ+}{\underset{+\circ}{}}$$

which may also be written as

$$\diagdown\!\!\!\!\diagup\ \text{O}{=}\text{O}\ \diagup\!\!\!\!\diagdown$$

where each line represents a pair of electrons, one of each spin. Such a structure is consistent with what has already been said here about electronic structures. It is easy to see, from the above formulae, that the four pairs on each atom can be disposed tetrahedrally, two pairs being shared and two pairs being lone on each atom. Each atom has round it a roughly tetrahedral group of four electrons of one spin, and a similar group of four electrons of the other spin. For those of each spin, the tetrahedron centred on one nucleus shares a common edge with the tetrahedron centred on the other nucleus. The above formulae imply that the electrons of one spin are disposed similarly in space to those of the other. In this case all electrons will occur in spatial pairs (i.e. there are six pairs; see Fig. 16). Experimentally it is found that this represents the electronic structure of the excited state of O_2 which is 38 kcal above the ground state (the excited $^1\Sigma_g^+$ state). Another possibility exists when there are six electrons having each spin. This is that the two linked pairs of tetrahedra (each pair of tetrahedra involving six electrons of one spin)

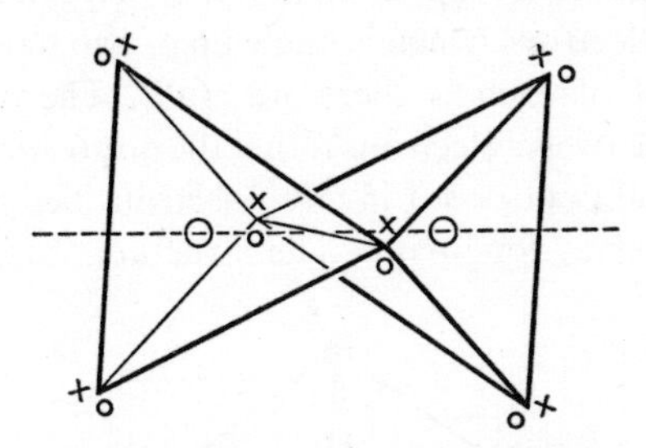

FIG. 16. Diagram of twelve electrons arranged as six pairs at the corners of two tetrahedra having a common edge between the nuclei. Diagrammatic representation of the arrangement of high probability for the $^1\Sigma_g^+$ state of O_2.

can have no favoured orientation relative to one another. The energy of such a state will be expected to be lower, because by allowing the electrons to be apart for 'part of the time', it reduces the average magnitude of the inter-electron repulsion energy. Such a state does exist (the $^1\Delta_g$ state) and is, in fact, the first excited state of the oxygen molecule, but its energy is still 23 kcal above that of the ground state.

There is still another possibility for O_2. The molecule might contain more electrons of one spin than of the other. Let us consider the case of seven electrons of one spin and five of the other. The seven could be arranged as

$$\begin{matrix}\times & & & & \times\\ \times & O & \times & O & \times\\ \times & & & & \times\end{matrix},$$

and the five as

$$\circ\; O \begin{matrix}\circ\\ \circ\\ \circ\end{matrix} O\; \circ .$$

The most probable disposition of the seven in the first set will be at the corners of two tetrahedra, one centred on each nucleus, with a common apex between the atoms. The most probable disposition of the second set is at the five corners of the body formed by two tetrahedra having a common face. Such an arrangement may be represented by the formula

$$\circ \substack{\times\\ \times\\ \times} \mathrm{O} \substack{\circ\\ \circ\\ \circ} \times \mathrm{O} \substack{\times\\ \times\\ \times} \circ$$

(see Fig. 17). From this, it is apparent that each oxygen has, in the valence shell, an octet of electrons which is made up of two tetrahedral spin-sets. The valence shell of each is therefore 'full'. The advantage of this arrangement of the twelve electrons is that the disposition of the positions of highest probability does not involve electrons being in 'close-pairs', either in bonds, or as lone-pairs. The structure therefore results in a

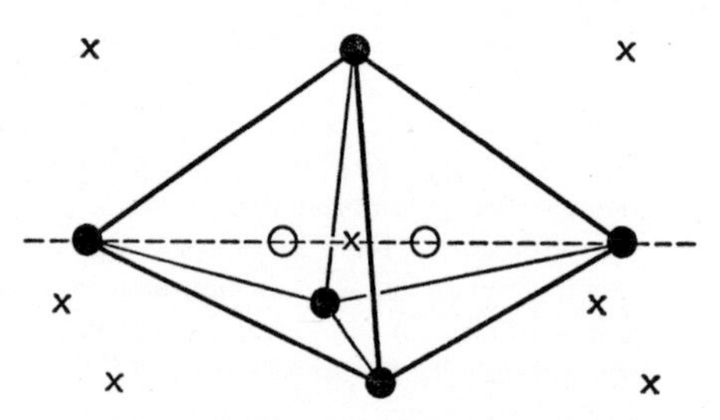

FIG. 17. Diagram of electron arrangement of high probability for the ground state of O_2 ($^3\Sigma_g^-$). Five electrons (circles) as two tetrahedra with a common face (shown); seven electrons (crosses) as two tetrahedra (not shown, cf. Fig. 15), with a common apex.

reduction in the mean inter-electronic repulsion energy and, as a consequence, the energy of this state will be expected to be lower than those of the states considered earlier, for which the mean inter-electronic repulsion energy will be greater. It is in fact the ground state of the oxygen molecule (the $^3\Sigma_g^-$ state), the magnetic moment of which shows that it contains two more electrons of one spin than of the other.

It is impossible that the oxygen molecule could exist stably having eight electrons of one spin and four of the other. To achieve the same concentration of electrons in the bond region as for the three states so far considered in this section, the eight electrons of one spin would have to be disposed as

$$\substack{\times\\ \times\\ \times\\ \times} \mathrm{O} \quad \mathrm{O} \substack{\times\\ \times\\ \times\\ \times},$$

and the four of the other as

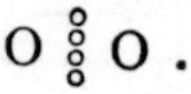

O oooo O .

With this pattern each atom has associated with it four electrons of each spin. However, an essential feature of the approach used in this book is that the electrons of each spin should have a high probability of being disposed tetrahedrally. This is impossible for the four in the internuclear region (this impossibility is the reason why no bonds of higher order than triple bonds have ever been observed). Also the eight electrons

TABLE 2

State	Energy per g mol above ground state (kcal)	Equilibrium length Å	Electronic arrangement		Relative disposition of two sets
			One set	Other set	
$^1\Sigma_g^+$	38	1·227	 oo O oo O oo	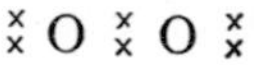 xx O xx O xx	Same spatial disposition (Fig. 16)
$^1\Delta_g$	23	1·216	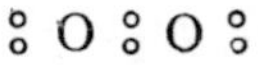 oo O oo O oo	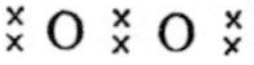 xx O xx O xx	No correlation between sets
$^3\Sigma_g^-$	0	1·207	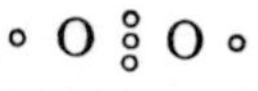 o O ooo O o	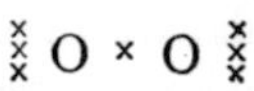 xxx O x O xxx	(Fig. 17)

(four separately round each nucleus; the crosses above) would produce strong repulsion because the system resembles, as far as the electrons of this spin are concerned, two inert gas atoms. In agreement with this, no low-lying energy states of O_2 are known for which the magnetic moment corresponds to there being four more electrons of one spin than of the other.

The patterns of the three low-lying states are depicted in Table 2. From this it can be seen that all three states have four electrons in the bond region, and this is probably the reason why the equilibrium bond lengths are the same (1·217 ± 0·010). The pattern of the energies is very reasonable. The ground state, by giving to each set a different disposition, keeps the electrons apart the most successfully. The highest of the three has two spin-sets which, as far as the effects of spin correlation are

4

concerned, tend to be coincident, so the mean inter-electron repulsion energy is a maximum. The middle state has each spin-set the same as those in the highest state. However, there is no spin-correlation between the two sets. Therefore the mean inter-electronic repulsion energy will be intermediate between those for the other two states. The spacing of the three states on an energy scale is fairly even.

The reason why the ground state of O_2 has a magnetic moment corresponding to two unpaired electrons is successfully explained by the method of constructing and describing the orbitals of a molecule which is known as the *molecular orbital method*. The treatment is equivalent to the present one, and also leads to the conclusion that the reason this particular state is the ground state is the reduction in inter-electronic repulsion energy that occurs for that electron configuration.

3.3 The Nitrogen Molecule and Related Species

In this molecule there are ten electrons in the valence shell. In the ground state the molecule has a zero magnetic moment, so there must be five electrons to each spin. In this configuration of highest probability, the five electrons of each set will be situated at the corners of two tetrahedra having a common face. That is, the two sets will be arranged as

$$\times\,\mathrm{N}\,\overset{\times}{\underset{\times}{\times}}\,\mathrm{N}\,\times \quad \text{and} \quad \circ\,\mathrm{N}\,\overset{\circ}{\underset{\circ}{\circ}}\,\mathrm{N}\,\circ\,.$$

The two triangular sets in the bond region may be staggered with respect to one another without affecting the tetrahedral disposition round each atom; this will tend to reduce inter-electronic repulsion and may be one of the factors contributing to the strength of this triple bond. There will also be two lone-pairs, one on each nitrogen atom. It is probable that, because the *bonding* electrons are drawn to the bond axis by the dual effect of the two nuclei, the lone-pair orbitals may be diffuse and relatively extensive, so that inter-electron repulsion between the members of these lone-pairs may not be particularly high. This would also be a contributing factor to the low energy and stability of the system.

It is interesting that this model, while not disposing of the electrons in the bond as spatial pairs, places the electrons outside the bond as two pairs. It is, therefore, easy to see that the electronic structure of acetylene will resemble that of nitrogen; the electrons in $C_2^{=}$ (iso-electronic with N_2) outside the bond region will be suitably disposed, as two spatial pairs, to form strong bonds to two protons and a stable linear HCCH.

Iso-electronic with N_2 are CO, CN^- and NO^+. Their bond lengths are: N_2, 1·094 Å; CO, 1·128 Å; CN^-, 1·15 Å; and NO^+, 1·062 Å. The lengths show that all the bonds are essentially similar; small changes result from changes in the nuclear charge, high nuclear charges leading to shorter bonds, and small to longer bonds. These three species, CO, CN^- and NO^+, must therefore have electronic structures similar to that of the nitrogen molecule, as shown diagrammatically early in this section. Because the nuclear charges differ the sharing of the electrons by the two centres must be unequal. Evidence that this effect occurs is provided by the *small* dipole moment of CO. The presence of a lone-pair of electrons on the carbon atom in carbon monoxide,

$$\substack{\circ\\\times}\ \mathrm{C}\ \substack{\circ\\\circ\\\circ}\substack{\times\\\times\\\times}\ \mathrm{O}\ \substack{\circ\\\times}$$

and in the cyanide ion,

$$\substack{\circ\\\times}\ \mathrm{C}\ \substack{\circ\\\circ\\\circ}\substack{\times\\\times\\\times}\ \mathrm{N}\ \substack{\circ\\\times}\ ,$$

would be expected to be a source of instability however (ordinarily carbon ions are unstable). This will be greater in CN^- than in CO, because the oxygen nucleus draws the electron distribution towards itself in CO more than does the nitrogen nucleus in CN^-. Consequently the lone-pair on the carbon in CN^- is more reactive than that in CO. Thus CN^- is a weak acid and will readily take a proton from water to give HCN (cf. earlier remarks about HCCH). This neutralizes the charge unsatisfactorily concentrated in that lone-pair in CN^-. The cyanide ion also readily donates electrons to metal ions to form cyanide complexes (e.g. $Fe(CN)_6^{3-}$). In fact distinct CN^- is only found with certainty in the lattices with alkali metal ions. There it is stabilized by the high field provided by the surrounding alkali metal ions which, themselves, have a low electron affinity, relative to other positive ions. In CO the lone-pair on the carbon is more stable than that in CN^-. However, it does form complexes such as $Ni(CO)_4$ in which the pair is shared with a metal atom. Also the ion HCO^+ is believed to be one of the most important ions in hydrocarbon–air flames (Calcote, 9th Combustion Symposium, 1963). This is understandable, if the stability of the lone-pair on the carbon atom is improved by sharing with a proton.

3.4 The Nitric Oxide Molecule

In the nitric oxide molecule there are eleven electrons in the valence shell to be considered. It is a paramagnetic substance, and the numerical value of the magnetic moment shows that, in the molecule, there is one more electron of one spin than of the other; that is, there are six of one, and five of the other. The equilibrium bond length is 1·15 Å which is intermediate between that in N_2 (1·06 Å) and O_2 (1·21 Å). The vibration frequency of NO, in its ground state, is 1876 cm^{-1} which is intermediate between that of N_2 (2330 cm^{-1}) and that of O_2 (1556 cm^{-1}). These results show clearly that the bond in NO is intermediate between that in N_2 consisting of six electrons, and that in O_2, consisting of four electrons. Therefore it must be presumed that the bond in NO, in its ground state, contains five electrons. Moreover it is important to realize that these figures show that no abnormal instability is conferred on the molecule because it contains an odd number of electrons; its dissociation energy is 150 kcal/g mol which is intermediate between that for N_2 (225 kcal/g mol) and for O_2 (117 kcal/g mol).

From what has been said earlier, the six electrons of one spin would be expected to be disposed as

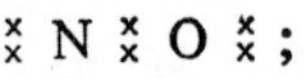

$$\substack{\times\\ \times}\,\mathrm{N}\,\substack{\times\\ \times}\,\mathrm{O}\,\substack{\times\\ \times}\,;$$

that is, at the corners of two tetrahedra which have a common edge between the nuclei. The five electrons of the other spin would be expected to be disposed as

$$\circ\,\mathrm{N}\,\substack{\circ\\ \circ\\ \circ}\,\mathrm{O}\,\circ\,;$$

that is, at the corners of two tetrahedra which have a common base between the nuclei. The total structure may therefore be represented by

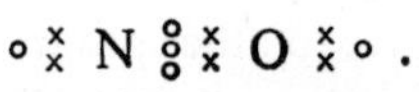

$$\circ\substack{\times\\ \times}\,\mathrm{N}\,\substack{\circ\\ \circ\\ \circ}\substack{\times\\ \times}\,\mathrm{O}\,\substack{\times\\ \times}\circ\,.$$

Each atom has an octet of electrons made up of four electrons of one spin and four of the other. The valence shell of each atom is therefore 'full'.

This electronic structure is a very satisfactory one because it reduces inter-electronic repulsion. It explains how it is possible to form a stable molecule from a nitrogen atom and an oxygen atom, the five-electron bond having properties which show that the order is intermediate between the bonds in N_2 (six electron) and O_2 (four electron).

The iso-electronic O_2^+ has recently been observed in crystalline

O_2PtF_6 (Bartlett and Lohmann, *Proc. C.S.*, 1962). The bond length is about 1·17 Å. This is consistent with the structure

$$\circ\overset{\times}{\underset{\times}{}}\,O\,\overset{\circ}{\underset{\circ}{}}\overset{\times}{\underset{\times}{}}\,O\,\overset{\times}{\underset{\times}{}}\circ\,.$$

It is, of course, like all other ions only stable when present in a favourably electrostatic environment; in this case, in a crystal, surrounded by negative ions.

The particular question that presents itself with nitric oxide is: Why does NO not dimerize to N_2O_2 since it has an odd number of electrons?

Lewis must have been surprised that nitric oxide did not dimerize to N_2O_2 having the electronic structure

$$\rangle O{=}\underset{|}{N}{-}\overset{|}{N}{=}O\langle\ ,$$

which contains an even number of electrons, five bonding electron-pairs and six lone-pairs. However, two nitric oxide molecules taken together also contain ten bonding-electrons and twelve unshared electrons. Consequently dimerization would not lead to any increase in the number of bonding electrons, and therefore it cannot be expected that there will be any large gain energetically. The situation is quite different from some other species containing an odd number of electrons; say two methyl radicals or two fluorine atoms. Two methyl radicals have, taken together, six CH bonds. Ethane, formed by the combination of two methyl radicals, contains six CH bonds and one CC bond. On dimerization there is therefore an increase in the number of bonding electrons. Likewise when two fluorine atoms combine, a new two-electron bond is formed. On the basis of this argument it can be understood why the odd-electron molecule NO behaves differently from atoms such as F, and radicals such as CH_3, NH_2 or OH.

There is also reason to expect the molecule

$$\rangle O{=}\underset{|}{N}{-}\overset{|}{N}{=}O\langle$$

to be less stable energetically than two 'molecules' of NO. In the dimer, the electrons of one spin adopt the same spatial pattern as the electrons of the other spin. For each pair, therefore, the two electrons occupy the same spatial region. Because there are eleven pairs, this leads to a considerable inter-electron repulsion energy. In the monomer, the electrons of one spin adopt a different pattern from electrons of the other spin. Hence in the monomer it will be expected that inter-electron repulsion will be relatively less important than it would be in the dimer. This operates to stabilize the monomer relative to the dimer.

There are two situations in which an association of two nitric oxide molecules occurs. In solid nitric oxide, molecules occur in pairs, the atoms being at the corners of a rectangle. Two sides of the rectangle have virtually the same lengths as the bonds in monomeric NO (1·12 Å). The other two sides are very long (2·4 Å) and the distance suggests that there are no ordinary chemical bonds between the two NO. Certainly the structure is not that shown earlier in the section. If nitric oxide is condensed in a matrix of solid argon at liquid helium temperatures some association of NO molecules occurs (Fateley, Bent and Crawford, *J.C.P.*, 1959). However, the associated pair has NO vibration frequencies (1768 and 1862 cm^{-1}) which are characteristic of bonds of much higher order than 2. (The characteristic frequency for an NO double bond is *ca.* 1550 cm^{-1}.) This pair of frequencies has also been observed in liquid nitric oxide by Smith, Keller and Johnston (1770 and 1863 cm^{-1}, *J.C.P.*, 1951). It is not known with certainty that these frequencies arise from a pair of NO molecules associated with one another, but, if they do, then the electronic structure of the pair is certainly not

$$\rangle O = \underset{|}{N} - \overset{|}{N} = O \langle \; .$$

The fact that this system has been investigated extensively, and yet there is no evidence for a dimer of this structure, suggests that this electronic arrangement is indeed an unstable one relative to two NO. This system therefore appears to provide a good example of the energetic disadvantage of the spatial 'pairing' of electrons when other alternatives which involve the same number of bonding electrons are possible.

3.5 Formal Charges

In the remainder of this book some use will be made of so-called formal charges. These are calculated for atoms, covalently bound in molecules, by summing algebraically the charges associated with the atom according to the following simple rules. The nuclear charge is treated as being fully associated with the atom, the charges on the inner-shell and unshared electrons are treated as being fully associated with the atom, the charges on electrons shared in a bond by two atoms are assigned a half to each atom. For any structure it is then very easy and straightforward to calculate the formal charges on each atom. This is one of the advantages of this procedure; that is, there will be no uncertainty between different workers what the values of the formal charges for any specified structure are. On the other hand, formal charges do not have any real physical significance or real existence. They must therefore be used cautiously. In this book, the values for the various electronic structures considered will be calculated. The formal charges that are likely to be allowable energetically will be decided by comparison with other simple species which are known to exist, and for which the formal charges can be calculated with certainty because the structures are clearly known. The four atoms, F, O, N and C will now be considered.

Fluorine readily gives the fluoride ion in which the formal charge on the fluorine is -1. It exists in stable fluorides such as CH_3—F in which the formal charge is zero. Pauling has proposed that structures in which the fluorine has a formal charge of $+1$ have some importance (e.g. $F^-CH_2=F^+$ in CH_2F_2). However this needs to be examined more closely. Liquid hydrogen fluoride has been studied extensively as a solvent. It is excellent for forming positive ions by donating a proton, the negative ion present being FHF^-. However it is only in extreme circumstances that it will yield H_2F^+. The species certainly seems to exist when $HClO_4$ or BF_3 is added, the ions present being in the two cases H_2F^+ and ClO_4^-, and H_2F^+ and BF_4^-. A crystalline compound is known having the formula $HF.HClO_4$ and this very probably contains H_2F^+ and ClO_4^-. Thus there are circumstances in which H—F$^+$—H, in which the fluorine has a formal positive charge, can be formed. However, the circumstances must be as extreme as possible, and it is quite clear that ordinarily fluorine will not take on a formal positive charge of $+1$.

The molecule BF_3 is a stable one but it is a strong electron acceptor, readily forming a coordinate link with a molecule possessing a lone-pair of electrons; for example $R_3N{:}BF_3$. It is generally believed that, in BF_3, there is some coordination of electrons from the fluorine to the boron, producing a bonding additional to the three single BF bonds. This is possible because, with three single bonds, boron would have a valence shell of only six electrons. If back coordination occurred to the extent of adding two electrons to the valence shell of boron, then the formal charge on the boron atom would be -1. Assuming then that the compensating formal positive charge is equally divided between the boron atoms, each will have $+\frac{1}{3}$. When an electron donor forms a coordinate link with the boron (as above), the formal charge on the fluorine drops to zero. If the back coordination involved a full transfer of two electrons, there would be no increase in the number of bonding electrons on coordination, and, the advantage gained in the reaction would be the removal of the formal positive charge from the fluorine atoms. On the other hand, if there were to be a gain in the number of bonding electrons (as must happen with BMe_3) then the average formal charge on the fluorine atoms is less than $+\frac{1}{3}$. For this reason we shall treat $+\frac{1}{3}$ as the limiting formal positive charge that is allowed on a fluorine atom. It will imply that, if there is a single structure with a formal positive charge of $+\frac{1}{2}$, such a molecule will not exist, but if there are several possible electronic structures, in some of which a fluorine atom carries a formal charge of $+\frac{1}{2}$, then the molecule may be stable (see discussion of Resonance in section 4.3).

Oxygen forms H_3O^+ and OH^-. The ion H_4O^{++} is not known and $O^=$ only exists when stabilized by a strong field produced by a number of positive ions (see section 2.3). The ion H_3O^+ exists in crystals and in a solvated form in water. It is probably fair to conclude therefore that structures in which the oxygen atom assumes a formal charge of $+\frac{1}{2}$ can be very important, and those in which it assumes a formal charge of $+1$ can be reasonably important. The situation is similar for OH^-. It exists in crystals and in a solvated form in aqueous solution. It may be assumed therefore that structures in which oxygen atoms assume formal charges of $-\frac{1}{2}$ can be very important, and that those in which it carries a formal charge of -1 can only be fairly important. Therefore one can safely assume that structures in which the formal charge on an oxygen atom lies in the range $-\frac{1}{2}$ to $+\frac{1}{2}$ can be highly important, while those in the range -1 to $-\frac{1}{2}$, and $+\frac{1}{2}$ to $+1$, can be of some importance.

Nitrogen is known with a formal charge of $+1$ in NH_4^+ and of -1 in NH_2^-. The ammonium ion is stable in solution and also in many crystals of ammonium salts. Therefore it is reasonable to suppose that a nitrogen atom can assume a formal charge of $+1$ readily. The amide ion NH_2^- is, however, only known in much more extreme circumstances. Thus it exists in sodamide $NaNH_2$, where it is undoubtedly stabilized only because there is an array of positively charged sodium ions of low electron affinity round it. Thus it must therefore be supposed that the nitrogen atom can only assume a charge of -1 under rather extreme circumstances, and hence that structures in which there is a nitrogen atom carrying a formal charge of -1 will be of limited importance. However, it is perhaps not unreasonable to suppose that a structure in which a nitrogen atom has a charge of $-\frac{1}{2}$ can be fairly important.

The results of these considerations regarding allowable formal charges are summarized in Table 3.

The situation regarding the carbon atom is rather different, because it forms four strong electron-pair bonds so readily and then has a formal charge of zero. Any structure in which carbon carries either a formal positive or negative charge must also result in the carbon atom forming a smaller number of bonds; usually three. This operates against structures in which the carbon carries any formal charge. In the cyanide ion and in carbon monoxide, the carbon atom has a formal charge of -1. This ion and this molecule were discussed in section 3.4. The ion is only

TABLE 3

This Table lists the formal charges that are *satisfactory* in structures of considerable importance and *possible* in those of minor importance.

Atom	Satisfactory	Possible
F	-1 to $+\frac{1}{3}$	$+\frac{1}{2}$
O	$-\frac{1}{2}$ to $+\frac{1}{2}$	$+1$ and -1
N	$-\frac{1}{2}$ to $+1$	-1 (just)

stabilized when in a lattice surrounded by alkali metal ions. On the other hand, carbon monoxide is a very stable molecule and it seems that this is one of the few cases where the concept of formal charges is unhelpful and even misleading. Ordinarily it would have been expected that a charge of -1 on carbon and of $+1$ on oxygen would cause unstability. This must be compensated in part by an electron shift from the carbon towards the oxygen, and in part by the great strength of a triple bond between two atoms in the first short period (cf. N_2, NO^+, CN^-). In the ordinary way, it is probably safe to assume that structures in which the carbon atoms carries a charge more negative than $-\frac{1}{2}$ are of little importance. The ion CH_4^+ is stable in the mass spectrometer, and it is reasonable to suppose that here the carbon carries some positive charge. So perhaps structures in which the carbon atom carries a charge of $+\frac{1}{2}$ should not be ignored. However, we shall find that in the large majority of structures with which we shall be concerned, the carbon atom carries a zero formal charge and forms bonds involving all eight electrons in the valence shell.

3.6 Other Odd-electron Diatomic Molecules

In section 3.4 the electronic structure of NO was considered and it was found that a satisfactory double-quartet structure exists which accounts for its stability. If it is possible to form a stable diatomic molecule from the First Row element of Group V and the one of Group VI, the following obvious questions present themselves: Would we expect a diatomic molecule formed by the elements of Group IV and of Group V to be stable? Would we expect a diatomic molecule formed by the elements of Group VI and of Group VII to be stable?

Let us take the first question and consider the cyanide radical CN. This has nine electrons in the valence shell. If there are five of one spin and four of the other, the five could have the disposition

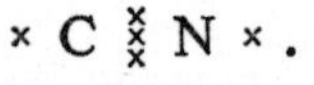

$$\times\ \mathrm{C}\ \begin{smallmatrix}\times\\ \times\\ \times\end{smallmatrix}\ \mathrm{N}\ \times\ .$$

However, the other four cannot be located simultaneously in the bond region because of the need for them to be disposed tetrahedrally round the nucleus (this situation was encountered and discussed with N_2). The two possibilities for the ground state are therefore

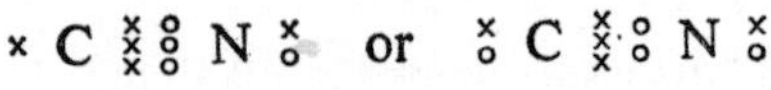

$$\times\ \mathrm{C}\ \begin{smallmatrix}\times\\ \times\\ \times\end{smallmatrix}\begin{smallmatrix}\circ\\ \circ\\ \circ\end{smallmatrix}\ \mathrm{N}\ \begin{smallmatrix}\times\\ \circ\end{smallmatrix}\quad \text{or}\quad \begin{smallmatrix}\times\\ \circ\end{smallmatrix}\ \mathrm{C}\ \begin{smallmatrix}\times\\ \times\\ \times\end{smallmatrix}\cdot\begin{smallmatrix}\circ\\ \circ\end{smallmatrix}\ \mathrm{N}\ \begin{smallmatrix}\times\\ \circ\end{smallmatrix}$$

(or a resonance hybrid of these might provide the best description). The first of these has a bond order of three, and the second one of $2\frac{1}{2}$ (cf. section 9.2). Let us consider the dimer of CN, namely cyanogen, C_2N_2. The electronic structure of this will be

$$-\mathrm{N}\equiv\mathrm{C}-\mathrm{C}\equiv\mathrm{N}-\ .$$

This contains fourteen bonding-electrons, whereas 2CN cannot contain more than twelve and may contain less. Therefore 2CN will be unstable relative to C_2N_2 in the way that $2CH_3$ are unstable relative to C_2H_6, and 2F are unstable relative to F_2. Hence CN (Group IV and V) will not be expected to be a stable molecule like NO (Group V and VI).

Now, FO will be considered. This has thirteen valence-shell electrons. If there are six electrons of one spin, and seven of the other (and it is found that no other division is sensible), the electronic structure will be

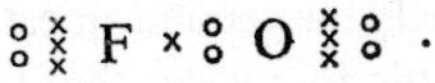

$$\substack{\circ\\ \circ}\ \substack{\times\\ \times\\ \times}\ \mathrm{F}\ \times\ \substack{\circ\\ \circ}\ \mathrm{O}\ \substack{\times\\ \times\\ \times}\ \substack{\circ\\ \circ}\ .$$

This has three bonding electrons and, since F—O—O—F has six, the same arguments might be used for the stability of the monomer as were used with NO. However, there is a serious objection to the above formula for FO, which is that the fluorine atom carries a formal charge of $+\frac{1}{2}$ (that on O is $-\frac{1}{2}$). Reference to Table 3 shows that the arguments used in section 3.5 lead to the view that such a structure will be one of high energy. Experimentally it is found that FOOF exists at low temperatures but at about -100°C decomposes into F_2 and O_2. Presumably the reason why F_2 and O_2 are stable relative to 2FO is that, in them, the formal atomic charges are all zero, and in O_2, inter-electron repulsion is reduced (see section 3.3). Consequently it is understandable that 2FO should be unstable relative to O_2 and F_2. The dimer F_2O_2 will be considered further in section 5.7.

The adverse formal charge situation in FO does not exist in NO. With the five-electron bond, the formal charges on the nitrogen and oxygen atoms are respectively $-\frac{1}{2}$ and $+\frac{1}{2}$. It can be seen from Table 3 that these are satisfactory.

The O_2^- ion is iso-electronic with FO and the structure may presumably be written as

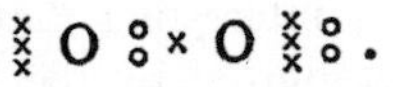

$$\substack{\circ\\ \circ}\ \substack{\times\\ \times\\ \times}\ \mathrm{O}\ \substack{\circ\\ \circ}\ \times\ \mathrm{O}\ \substack{\times\\ \times\\ \times}\ \substack{\circ\\ \circ}\ .$$

In this case, the formal charges on the two atoms are satisfactory, being $-\frac{1}{2}$ on both. The bond length (1·28 Å) is consistent with the above formulation, since it is intermediate between the four-electron bond in O_2 (1·21 Å), and the two-electron one in HO—OH (1·48 Å). This so-called superoxide ion is known in KO_2, RbO_2 and CsO_2. It exists stably when the field provided by the positive ions is not sufficiently high to stabilize either $O^=$ or $O_2^=$ as the preferred ions; that is, when the positive ions are large and carry only a single charge (K^+, Rb^+ and Cs^+). It is a matter of some interest that, in KO_2 for example, the oxygen exists in the crystal entirely as paramagnetic O_2^-, this being formed by heating potassium in O_2. The ion contains an odd number of electrons and, in this environment, does not disproportionate to O_2 and $O_2^=$, both of which contain an even number of electrons. This provides another example of the fact that, in a suitable situation, species containing an odd number of electrons can be preferred to those containing an even number.

Consequently, as regards the second question posed at the beginning of this section, it is possible to answer that OF (containing atoms from Group VI and VII) is not stable, even though NO is, for reasons which can be understood, but that O_2^-, which is iso-electronic with OF, is stable showing that a three-electron bond can have the required strength and stability.

3.7 Other Diatomic Ions

The other $O_2^{=}$ will be expected to have an electronic structure similar to that of F_2 (section 3.2). In this structure each oxygen atom has formal charge of -1, which is rather unsatisfactory (see Table 3). This is consistent with the behaviour of this ion. It exists in crystals such as those of Li_2O_2, Na_2O_2 and RaO_2. In all these the field at the $O_2^{=}$ ion, produced by the positive ions, is considerable because, though Li^+ and Na^+ are only singly charged, they are small and because Ba^{++} carries a double charge. Thus $O_2^{=}$ does exist, though only when stabilized by an appropriate electric field. The only other doubly charged diatomic ion is $C_2^{=}$ which exists in calcium carbide. There are probably two resaons for its existence. The first is that, in this crystal, it is surrounded by six doubly charged, not very large, calcium ions. The second is that it contains a triple bond which is strong when two atoms of the First Short Period are involved. It is interesting that these two doubly charged negative ions are both stabilized by the high fields provided by the doubly charged positive ions of group IIa (e.g. in CaC_2 and BaO_2). This demonstrates that a strong field is needed to stabilize them, as would be expected.

The negative ion NO^-, which is iso-electronic with O_2, is thought to exist but the evidence is by no means certain. It is sometimes stated that it is diamagnetic but the evidence for this also seems to be unreliable. It would be very interesting to have more reliable data for NO^-.

The OF^- ion might have been expected to exist. Its electronic structure would be expected to be similar to that of F_2, in which case the oxygen and fluorine atoms would carry formal charges of -1 and 0 respectively. However, the stability relative to the process

$$2OF^- \rightarrow O_2 + 2F^-$$

must be considered. Table 3 indicates that a formal charge of -1 on oxygen is not altogether satisfactory. Therefore the above process will be favoured because the negative charge is transferred from the oxygen atom to the more suitable fluorine atom. There is no change in the number of bonding electrons in the above reaction but because the electrons of opposite spin are separated from one another, both in O_2 and F^-, the right-hand side will probably also be favoured by a reduction in inter-electron repulsion energy. The one possibility of stabilizing OF^- might be under the influence of the field provided by an array of positive charges in a crystal. However, this is likely to be difficult or impossible to achieve, because the lattice energies of fluorides are high because the fluoride ion F^- is small. All these considerations suggest that it is unlikely that OF^- will ever be found, and, if it is, the circumstances will need to be very special ones.

3.8 Conclusion

In this chapter we have considered, with the exception of CN, only diatomic molecules, radicals and ions formed by the atoms C, N, O and F which contained ten, eleven, twelve, thirteen or fourteen electrons. Examples of each species are known:

Ten: N_2, CN^-, CO, NO^+; Eleven: NO, O_2^+; Twelve: O_2 (NO^-);
Thirteen: O_2^-; Fourteen: F_2, $O_2^{=}$.

These electronic systems were considered because, with them, structures are possible for which the valence shell of each atom is full, i.e. each atom has an octet of electrons. It has been found that, using the double-quartet hypothesis, it is possible to formulate satisfactory structures both for the species containing an odd as well as those containing an even number of electrons, and to understand their existence and stability. An additional and particular success of this approach has been that it accounts successfully for the paramagnetism of the ground state of O_2. With the help of the simple concept of formal charges it has been possible to eliminate certain possibilities; for instance, to understand why OF and OF^- are not known. Any discussion of valency must, of course, be just as successful in explaining why certain species do not exist as accounting for those that do. The performance of the present method for all diatomic molecules and ions containing ten to fourteen valence-shell electrons is shown in Table 4. This lists the formal charges on each atom for each of the fifty species. Those that are known by experiment to exist are marked by rectangles. If reference is made to the allowable formal charges in Table 3, it will be seen that the only one that might be expected to exist which does not is N_2^-. However, this would have formal charges of $-\frac{1}{2}$ on *both* nitrogen atoms. Perhaps this presence, on adjacent atoms, of two charges of $-\frac{1}{2}$ does, by their effect on one another, render the system unstable. The ions $C_2^{=}$, CN^-, NO^+ and $O_2^{=}$

TABLE 4

The table lists the formal charges on each atom in the order listed on the left, it being presumed that bonds of the order 3, $2\frac{1}{2}$, 2, $1\frac{1}{2}$ and 1 are formed when there are ten, eleven, twelve, thirteen and fourteen electrons present. The rectangles mark the species that are known.

Diatomic molecule	Number of electrons				
	Ten	Eleven	Twelve	Thirteen	Fourteen
CC	$\boxed{-1/-1}$	$-1\frac{1}{2}/-1\frac{1}{2}$	$-2/-2$	$-2\frac{1}{2}/-2\frac{1}{2}$	$-3/-3$
CN	$\boxed{-1/0}$	$-1\frac{1}{2}/-\frac{1}{2}$	$-2/-1$	$-2\frac{1}{2}/-1\frac{1}{2}$	$-3/-2$
CO	$\boxed{-1/+1}$	$-1\frac{1}{2}/+\frac{1}{2}$	$-2/0$	$-2\frac{1}{2}/-\frac{1}{2}$	$-3/-1$
CF	$-1/+2$	$-1\frac{1}{2}/+1\frac{1}{2}$	$-2/+1$	$-2\frac{1}{2}/+\frac{1}{2}$	$-3/0$
NN	$\boxed{0/0}$	$-\frac{1}{2}/-\frac{1}{2}$	$-1/-1$	$-1\frac{1}{2}/-1\frac{1}{2}$	$-2/-2$
NO	$\boxed{0/+1}$	$\boxed{-\frac{1}{2}/+\frac{1}{2}}$	$-1/0$	$-1\frac{1}{2}/-\frac{1}{2}$	$-2/-1$
NF	$0/+2$	$-\frac{1}{2}/+1\frac{1}{2}$	$-1/+1$	$-1\frac{1}{2}/+\frac{1}{2}$	$-2/0$
OO	$+1/+1$	$\boxed{+\frac{1}{2}/+\frac{1}{2}}$	$\boxed{0/0}$	$\boxed{-\frac{1}{2}/-\frac{1}{2}}$	$-1/-1$
OF	$+1/+2$	$+\frac{1}{2}/+1\frac{1}{2}$	$0/+1$	$-\frac{1}{2}/+\frac{1}{2}$	$-1/0$
FF	$+2/+2$	$+1\frac{1}{2}/+1\frac{1}{2}$	$+1/+1$	$+\frac{1}{2}/+\frac{1}{2}$	$\boxed{0/0}$

have rather high formal charges on one or both of the atoms. In each case, of course, the ion only exists in a crystal where it is stabilized by the field provided by positive ions located around it. It is probable that NO^- also exists but again this will only be so when nearby positive ions exert a stabilizing effect. The only serious fault in this chart is the existence and high stability of CO. This is undoubtedly a result of the fact that there is a formal charge of $+1$ on one atom and -1 on the adjacent one, and a displacement of the electrons must result in stabilization. It is worth noting here that NF, which also has formal charges of -1 and $+1$, does not exist as a correspondingly stable molecule. The reason for this is probably twofold: (*a*) with twelve electrons only a double bond will be possible whereas with CO there is the particular advantage of high stability of the triple bond; (*b*) with NF the formal charge of $+1$ is associated with a fluorine atom; even if there were some compensating drift of electrons, presumably a positive charge would remain on the fluorine atom, and this does not appear to be at all favourable energetically.

The molecules, ions and radicals can all be treated most satisfactorily by the method of molecular orbitals. For these diatomic species the formulation used in this chapter is very closely related indeed to that which can be derived using molecular orbitals. However, the present procedure stresses the local situation at each atom and employs this as the basis. The molecular orbital method deals with the whole molecule and does not reveal the situation at each atom in a way that is at all obvious. In some respects, and in particular for qualitative purposes, it is usually easier to extend, to more complicated molecules, the approach which focuses its attention on the local situations. It is, for instance, well suited to the discussion of the stability and shapes of triatomic and larger molecules. This extension will be the objective of most of the following chapters. As the molecules become more complicated the relationship to the molecular orbital approach becomes less and less clear. However, it should be remembered that, as far as these diatomic species are concerned, the connection is very close indeed.

Later in this book (Chapter 9) some consideration will be given to the electronic structures of some of the diatomic molecules, which have been considered here, in their excited states. It will be found that a discussion of these can be carried out along similar lines to those used in this chapter.

CHAPTER FOUR

Some Triatomic Molecules

4.1 Introduction

This chapter describes the extension of the ideas outlined in Chapter 2, and applied in Chapter 3 to diatomic molecules and ions. The species discussed in this chapter will be mainly triatomic, but some consideration will be given, where appropriate, to those which contain more than three atoms. However, before this can be done, two matters require some further study. The first of these is the formulation that is to be used for the structures proposed. This will be dealt with in section 4.2. The second is that some preliminary and general consideration must be given to those situations in which it is possible to write several electronic formulae for the same molecule. This has been a most important feature of valency theory during the last twenty-five years, and is usually described by saying that 'resonance' occurs among the different structures, and that the true electronic structure is a resonance hybrid of these structures. This will be dealt with in section 4.3.

4.2 Formulae to be Used

In Chapters 2 and 3 electronic formulae were represented by using crosses and circles to represent electrons; the crosses and circles were used to differentiate the different spins of the various electrons; or perhaps this is described more exactly by saying that crosses and circles were used to indicate the spin that an electron situated in a particular region would be likely to have. This way of writing the structure is very satisfactory for the purpose that is required here but unfortunately it would become altogether too complicated for systems containing more atoms. It is therefore proposed that a line should be used to represent two electrons, one of each spin. This is, of course, current practice. By this means it is possible to simplify the formulae of the last chapter sufficiently.

However, a difficulty still remains which may be illustrated by considering the fluorine molecule. In F_2 there are two electrons, one of each spin, forming a bonding pair. That is, the two electrons may be supposed to be occupying the same spatial orbital (a bonding one) though there will be, of course, a degree of correlation between their positions, because they are both negatively charged. On the other hand, on each atom there are six unshared electrons, three of each spin. However, as discussed in the last chapter (section 3.2), the positions of these may be staggered relative to one another so that their spatial distribution would not be described by the same orbitals. Yet, on the above proposal these six electrons, three of each spin, would be represented by three lines. In order to differentiate these two types, a *heavy line* will be used to represent two electrons having opposite spins occupying the *same* spatial orbital (a pair), and a *light line* to represent two electrons on the same atom (or between the same pair of atoms) having opposite spins but *not* occupying the same orbital. With this the formula of F_2 becomes

$$-\overset{|}{\underset{|}{F}}-\overset{|}{\underset{|}{F}}-$$

and that of N_2 becomes

$$-N\equiv N-.$$

The formula of O_2, in its ground state, is

$$\overset{\times}{\underset{\times}{-}}O\overset{\circ}{\underset{\circ}{-}}O\overset{\times}{\underset{\times}{-}},$$

that of NO is

$$\overset{\times}{-}N\overset{\circ}{=}O\overset{\times}{-},$$

and that of O_2 is

$$\overset{\times}{=}O\overset{\circ}{-}O\overset{\times}{=}.$$

The formula of O_2 in the first excited state is

$$>O=O<,$$

and that of O_2 in the second excited state is

$$>O=O<.$$

The use of these heavy and light lines is not altogether satisfactory because the use of two types of lines complicates the formulae. However, the need to eliminate using individual symbols for individual electrons, and the need to be able to identify quickly the number of pairs occupying the same spatial orbital does, unfortunately, seem to make something of this kind necessary.

In some cases the use of crosses and circles to differentiate the spins associated with particular electrons is unnecessarily complicated. In such cases dots will be used to represent the individual electrons. Thus the formulae of O_2 and NO, in their ground states, would become

$$\div O \div O \div \quad \text{and} \quad \dot{-}N\dot{=}O\dot{-}\,.$$

It is now apparent that the above formulae are very similar to those used by Pauling who used in *The Nature of the Chemical Bond*, for O_2 and NO, the descriptions

$$-O\overset{\cdots}{\underset{\cdots}{\;}}O- \quad \text{and} \quad -N\overset{\cdots}{=}O-\,.$$

These have the disadvantage that they fail to make immediately clear two things: (*a*) that the binding provided by the three electrons represented by the three dots is about a half that of an electron-pair bond, this is to be expected at once with the present formula which gives a much truer impression of the electron distribution that exists; (*b*) that there are eight electrons in the region round each nucleus (excluding the K shell of two electrons) in these paramagnetic molecules as well as in the diamagnetic ones. In particular, as a result of (*b*), it is possible to extend the principles, that have been outlined, to more complicated systems.

It is worth repeating here that the bond in NO will, in this book, be described as a five-electron bond and not as two electron-pair single covalent bonds together with a three-electron bond (Pauling). The second gives a misleading idea of the electron pattern in space.

4.3 Existence of Several Electronic Structures

After Lewis had proposed his octet theory, in which he suggested also that a covalent bond consisted of a pair of electrons, it was realized that the electronic structure of many molecules could not be represented satisfactorily by a single formula of the Lewis type. The molecule of ozone will be taken as an example: the oxygen nuclei are at the corners of an isosceles triangle, the OOO angle being about $116\frac{3}{4}°$. Two Lewis formulae can be written for an arrangement in which two oxygen nuclei are bound to a third which is between them. They are

and

Neither of these alone is satisfactory because one, on its own, would imply that the two OO distances should be unequal, which they are not. Pauling therefore suggested that the electronic structure could, with advantage, be represented by a mixture or hybrid of these two, each contributing equally. In this way the equality of the two OO bond-lengths may be understood. Pauling described this situation by the word *resonance*, and supposed that it led to a lowering of energy relative to that expected theoretically for one of the forms alone.

In the last paragraph the words 'a mixture or hybrid' were used. In what sense are these words *mixture* and *hybrid* used? It may be supposed, in principle, that a wave-function can be written (according to some basic scheme, e.g. Heitler-London) which represents the first Lewis structure for ozone (Ψ_I). Also another can be written which represents the second (Ψ_{II}). Pauling proposed that the wave function of ozone could be written as

$$\Psi_{total} = N(\Psi_I + \Psi_{II})$$

where N is a numerical factor to keep the overall magnitude of the function correct (i.e. it is a scale factor).

For some molecules a wave function which is based on just one Lewis structure is reasonably satisfactory (e.g. F—O—F). In this case the *simple* Lewis formulation is adequate. On the other hand, with ozone, one Lewis structure is not adequate. Pauling, in effect, proposed that, in this situation, it was preferable to retain Lewis structures as the basis for our system of describing the electronic structures of molecules rather than to seek some new and additional basis. If this is done, and Lewis structures are retained as the basis, then it is necessary to use mixtures of wave functions as above (i.e. resonance). In a sense, the introduction of resonance is a confession of weakness. On the other hand it is surely too much to expect any reasonably simple basic method of formulating structures to be able to deal with the whole wide variety of molecules, ions and radicals that exist, using just one structure for each. No simple basis is likely to have this degree of flexibility. In such cases the method is likely to fall back on the *device* of describing those structures, that cannot be dealt with simply, as mixtures of the simple basic structures. As has been said, Pauling did this when he used Lewis structures as his basis, and the wave-mechanical development of this also adopts the same procedure. The same method is also used along with the molecular orbital method. In this case the separate simple basic structures are called configurations, and the mixing of the configurations is called *configuration interaction*.

It is probable that this procedure will be adopted along with any simple procedure for constructing the basis functions, at any rate for the time being. However, when a single basis structure is not adequate for constructing the ground state function, it is not necessarily true that mixing several members of this particular set of basis functions is a good way of arriving at a satisfactory wave function for the molecule or ion; though, of course, in the situation that exists it is the only way. In fact, it seems that for ozone the mixing of two Lewis structures (as above) is not really a good way of providing a good wave function for the ground state.

In effect the hypothesis being presented in this book involves a modification, or extension, of the basic way of constructing the first approximation wave functions for molecules and ions. It adds to the Lewis structures others which are new and different because the presence of pairs of electrons ocupying the different spatial orbitals (bond and lone-pair) is no longer a requirement. In some cases it eliminates the need to use resonance but, being a simple basis, it does not unfortunately eliminate completely the need to make some use of resonance. However by reducing the need for this device, it offers some advantages.

Finally, the form of mixing that is involved in resonance should be realized. It will be seen, from the formula given earlier in this section, that a wave function is constructed for each structure, and then *the wave functions are mixed* to give the total wave function. It is not a mixing of two electron distributions, but of two wave functions, and the mixed function has to be squared to yield the electron distribution. Consequently this includes, in addition to terms such as Ψ_{I}^2, terms containing $\Psi_{\mathrm{I}}\Psi_{\mathrm{II}}$. This is what makes the consequences of this mixing (i.e. of resonance) very difficult to understand physically with any precision. Largely because of this difficulty, the phrase 'stabilized by resonance' has become an extremely unsatisfactory one. It is not at all easy to relate this 'resonance energy' to any particular modifications of the kinetic and potential energy of the electronic system, and as a result it has become a phrase to be used in a rather facile and glib manner. Resonance has therefore developed an unreal quality, and every effort should certainly be made to reduce this part of valency theory which does not enhance, and often tends to obscure, our physical understanding. In this book an effort will be made to discuss the energetics of the systems that are examined in terms of factors such as inter-electronic repulsion energy, other forms of electrostatic energy and modifications to the kinetic energy of the electrons.

4.4 The Ozone Molecule and Nitrite Ion

In the last section, the ozone molecule was used as an example of one for which the simple Lewis formulation failed, and it was to meet this, and similar situations, that Pauling introduced *resonance*. On the hypothesis presented here another possibility exists, which is that the structure may be described best by a formula which can be written as

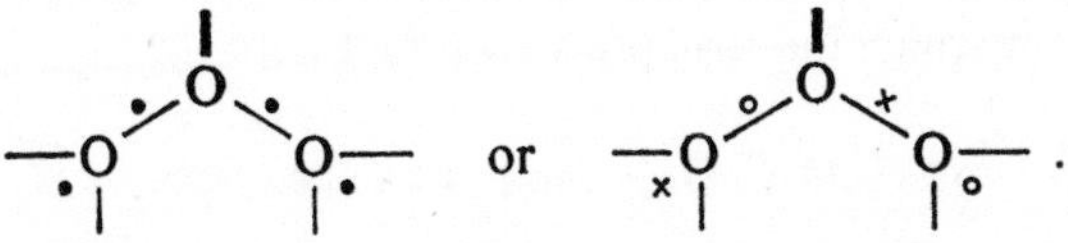

or .

Such a structure gives to each oxygen atom an octet of electrons, four of which have one spin, and four of which have the other. However, the electrons of one spin are disposed differently in space from those of the other as is brought out be setting out the two sets separately:

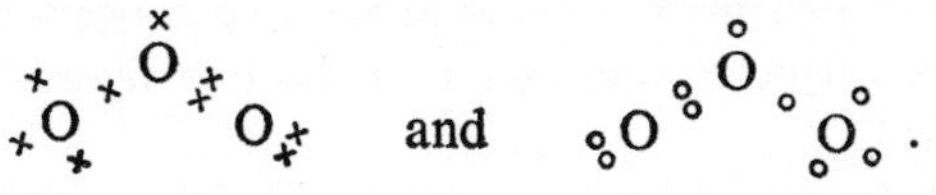

and .

Both sets would tend to produce an inter-bond angle in the neighbourhood of 120°. The experimental value is $116\frac{3}{4}$°. Both OO bonds are three electron bonds made up of two electrons of one spin and one of the other. They are therefore the same as the bond in O_2^-. The measured bond lengths in O_2^- and in O_3 are both 1·28 Å (cf. 1·21 in O_2 in its ground state (four electrons) and 1·48 in HO—OH (two electrons)). This formulation, therefore, accounts most satisfactorily for the shape of the molecule. The molecule of ozone is energetically more stable than would be expected for a structure $O{=}O{-}O$. For this the energy per molecule relative to $\frac{3}{2}O_2$ would be expected to be +61 kcal. This is made up of the energy needed to convert the rather special four-electron bond in the ground state of O_2 to a conventional double bond (+37), and half the dissociation energy of O_2 (+59) less the bond energy of an OO single bond (−35) (Cottrell, see Appendix). In fact, O_3 is only endothermic relative to $\frac{3}{2}O_2$ to the extent of 34 kcal/g mol. According to the Pauling resonance hypothesis using only Lewis structures, the gain of 27 kcal is to be described as 'resonance energy'. On the present method it is ascribed to a reduction in inter-electron repulsion energy in

$$\dot{=}O\dot{-}\overset{|}{O}\dot{-}O\dot{=}$$

relative to that to be expected in

$$=O=\overset{|}{O}-O\equiv .$$

This reduction in inter-electron repulsion energy of 34 kcal/g mol may be compared with the difference in energy of 37 kcal between the states of oxygen for which the structures proposed were

$$\div O\div O\div \quad \text{and} \quad =O=O= .$$

These two energies are very similar, which would be expected if both result from the same cause. It might have been argued that the effect in ozone would be expected to be half as big again as that in oxygen, because there are eighteen valence-shell electrons in the former, but only twelve in the latter. The ratio is, in fact, 0·9. However, there are other differences between the two systems which would make such a very simple approach unjustified. Nevertheless the fact that the two figures are so similar is satisfactory.

In the last section, it was suggested that resonance among Lewis structures might not really be a good method for constructing a satisfactory wave function. Calculations carried out by R. D. Gould and Miss M. H. Booth (Oxford) suggest that this is indeed the case. They have made calculations for the four electrons in the π-orbitals. In a valence bond structure two of these are located in one OO bond and the other two are, as a lone-pair, on the other oxygen atom. The other valence bond structure has the reverse disposition. The valence bond structure therefore assigns a high probability to a disposition in which two electrons are in the neighbourhood of an end atom. On the other hand, the double-quartet structure places one electron on the oxygen atom at one end of the molecule, one in the adjacent bond, one in the second bond, and one on the atom at the other end of the molecule. Thus both put two electrons in bond regions but the second distributes the electrons more evenly along the molecule. Mixing two structures, which give a high probability to distributions in which there are two electrons on an end atom, cannot possibly be equivalent to one in which the electronic charge is more evenly distributed. This may be put in another way. The Lewis structure O═O—O puts formal charges of O, +1 and −1 on the three atoms; the other Lewis structure puts, on the three atoms, the charges −1, +1 and 0. The structure

$$-\dot{O}\overset{\cdot}{-}O\overset{\cdot}{-}\dot{O}-,$$

on the other hand, places formal charges of $-\frac{1}{2}$, +1 and $-\frac{1}{2}$ on the three atoms. Because the form of the mixing used in resonance gives some weight to the distribution −1, +1 and 0 and 0, +1 and −1, this can never yield the same as the pattern of distribution $-\frac{1}{2}$, +1 and $-\frac{1}{2}$ which is suggested by the double-quartet structure. It is in this sense that mixing of, or resonance between, the two Lewis structures will not be equivalent to the double-quartet structure, and may not be suitable for obtaining a representation of the probable pattern of electron distributions.

The simple molecule orbital treatment of the four electrons in the π-orbitals of ozone has the great merit of being a straightforward one. Its weakness is that the electrons occupy orbitals which are the orbitals that would be appropriate to the system, if each electron were there separately, without the others. The simple M.O. treatment therefore includes nothing to allow for the effect of charge correlation, i.e. for the fact that the electrons tend to keep apart, because they all have the same charge. For this reason, calculations based on M.O. functions give too high a value to the inter-electron repulsion energy. It is because of this that the double-quartet structure leads to better results (i.e. a lower energy).

The conclusion is, therefore that the structure

$$-\dot{O}\overset{\cdot}{-}O\overset{\cdot}{-}\dot{O}-$$

provides the best *simple* description of the electronic structure of ozone. It accounts well for the bond length and bond angle, and qualitatively for the heat of formation from O_2.

The nitrite ion is iso-electronic with the ozone molecule. It is therefore assigned the electronic structure

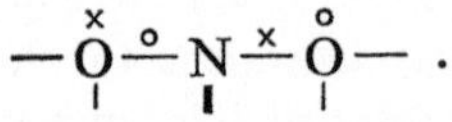

$$-\overset{\times}{\underset{|}{\mathrm{O}}}\overset{\circ}{-}\underset{|}{\mathrm{N}}\overset{\times}{-}\overset{\circ}{\underset{|}{\mathrm{O}}}- \ .$$

Calculations by D. M. Hirst (Oxford) have shown that a wave function based on this leads to a lower calculated energy than a function, based on a simple molecular orbital description, or one based on a valence bond formulation employing resonance between two Lewis structures (as for ozone). Again it is suggested that the reason why the above structure is adopted is that it separates the electrons of different spin from one another so reducing the inter-electron repulsion energy. Also it gives a satisfactory charge distribution, the formal charges on the three atoms are $-\frac{1}{2}$, 0, $-\frac{1}{2}$. Having regard to the fact that a charge of -1 must be accommodated by the ion, and that nitrogen does not assume a negative charge as readily as oxygen, this would seem to be a most satisfactory distribution of formal charges. Each of the Lewis structures has a formal charge distribution of the type 0, 0, -1, which is much less satisfactory.

The angle in NO_2^- is 115° which is not unreasonable for the above structure. The bond length is 1·24 Å which is somewhat shorter than would have been expected, since the length of the double bond in H—N═O is 1·21 Å.

The NO_2^- has a lone-pair on the nitrogen atom; the two electrons in this lone-pair are located in the same spatial region. In the nitro-compounds RNO_2, this lone-pair is used to bind the radical R to the nitrogen, being suitably disposed for this purpose. The structure of nitromethane is therefore

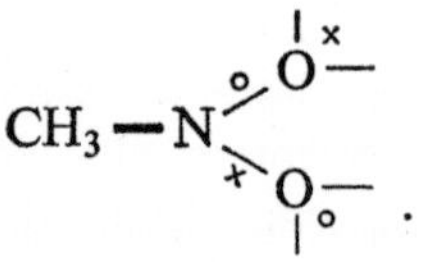

$$CH_3-N\begin{matrix} \overset{\circ}{\diagup}\ \overset{|\,\times}{\mathrm{O}}- \\ \underset{\times}{\diagdown}\ \underset{|\,\circ}{\mathrm{O}}- \end{matrix} \ .$$

The NO bond length in CH_3NO_2 is said to be 1·22 Å which is less than would have been expected. The reason for the shortness of the bond may be that the nitrogen carries a formal positive charge of $+1$ in CH_3NO_2 compared with zero in HNO. It is known that the presence of such a formal charge does lead to bond shortening. For example, the NN bond-length in hydrazine, $H_2N—NH_2$, is 1·47 Å whereas that in the hydrazinium ion, $H_3\overset{+}{N}—\overset{+}{N}H_3$, is 1·40 Å. The electron distribution in these nitro-compounds is expected to be a very satisfactory one because the electrons of each spin require the same shape for the molecule, and the electrons of one spin are separated from those of the other causing a reduction in inter-electron repulsion energy, and so leading to stabilization. There is much evidence which suggests that the nitro-group (NO_2) is a very stable group in many different molecules.

The molecule FNO also contains eighteen valence-shell electrons. Because it is worth considering along with CH_3NO, its electronic structure will not be discussed here. The structures of various nitroso compounds ANO will be considered in Chapter 5.

4.5 Carbon Dioxide and Iso-electronic Molecules and Ions

In the last section the electronic structures of O_3 and NO_2^- were discussed. These contain eighteen valence-shell electrons. In this section the triatomic species containing sixteen valence-shell electrons will be discussed. These are CO_2, N_2O, NO_2^+, N_3^-, NCO^- and $CN_2^{=}$.

For the CO_2 molecule the following electronic structures are possible:

4.I $\rangle O{=}C{=}O\langle$

4.II $-\overset{|}{\underset{|}{O}}-C\equiv O-$

4.III $-O\equiv C-\overset{|}{\underset{|}{O}}-$

4.IV $\overset{\times}{\underset{\times}{-}}O\overset{\circ}{\underset{\circ}{-}}C\overset{\times}{\underset{\times}{-}}O\overset{\circ}{\underset{\circ}{-}}$

4.V $\overset{\times}{-}\underset{|}{O}\overset{\circ}{-}C\overset{\times}{=}O\overset{\circ}{-}$

4.VI $\overset{\times}{-}O\overset{\circ}{=}C\overset{\times}{-}\underset{|}{O}\overset{\circ}{-}$.

These six structures place the following formal charges on the three atoms:

4.I 0, 0, 0; 4.III $+1, 0, -1$; 4.V $-\frac{1}{2}, 0, +\frac{1}{2}$;

4.II $-1, 0, +1$; 4.IV 0, 0, 0; 4.VI $+\frac{1}{2}, 0, -\frac{1}{2}$.

The conclusions summarized in Table 3 would suggest that 4.I, 4.IV, 4.V and 4.VI would be reasonable structures as far as the formal charges are concerned; 4.II and 4.III are likely to be much less important. Of the four, 4.IV will probably be the most important. Relative to 4.I, it separates the electrons of one spin from those of the other and so is likely to be of lower energy. Relative to 4.V and 4.VI it has zero formal charges on all three atoms, whereas the other two place formal charges on the two oxygen atoms. It is probable, therefore, that the best simple description is provided by 4.IV alone. However, an improvement would be provided for the ground state if some contribution of the electron distributions provided by 4.I, 4.V and 4.VI were also included.

Experiment shows that the CO_2 molecule is about 30 kcal/g mol more stable than would be expected for 4.I. The reaction:

$$2(CH_3)_2C{=}O \longrightarrow (CH_3)_4C + CO_2$$

is exothermic to the extent of 30 kcal/g mol (see Linnett, *J.A.C.S.*, 1961). On the hypothesis proposed here, this is primarily due to a reduction in interelectron repulsion energy in 4.IV, compared with 4.I. There are eight-electron pairs involved, so the energy saving per pair is less than in O_2. In O_2 there was a lowering of about 6 kcal/g mol per electron pair (37/6). In CO_2 there is about 4 kcal/g mol per electron pair (30/8). The reason for this may be the lower nuclear charge on carbon compared with oxygen, so that the orbitals are more diffuse; hence, in the pairs, electron repulsion is reduced. However, it is doubtful whether these proposals regarding inter-electron repulsion should be pushed so far quantitatively until more detailed consideration has been given to a wider range of examples. Nevertheless it is satisfying that the energy saving per pair is approximately the same value in the two systems. The bond length in CO_2 is 1·16 Å. This is shorter than the normal CO double bond in formaldehyde, the length of which is $1{\cdot}23 \pm 0{\cdot}02$. This is a surprising shortening for $C\div O$ relative to $C{=}O$, particularly as the $O{=}O$ bond is only a little longer than the $O\div O$ bond. It must be partly a consequence of replacing the two single CH bonds in H_2CO by a different electronic system. It will be found that NO_2^+ resembles CO_2 in this respect.

For the molecule NNO, six structures analogous to 4.I to 4.VI for CO_2 may be written. The formal charges are now:

4.I	$-1, +1, 0$;	4.III	$0, +1, -1$;	4.V	$-1\frac{1}{2}, +1, +\frac{1}{2}$;
4.II	$-2, +1, +1$;	4.IV	$-1, +1, 0$;	4.VI	$-\frac{1}{2}, +1, -\frac{1}{2}$.

Of these the only fully satisfactory one is 4.VI; the others place larger formal charges on one or other of the end atoms (or both). From this it is concluded that the NN bond should be a five-electron one and the NO bond should be a three-electron one. The bond lengths in N_2O are found to be: NN, 1·13 Å; NO, 1·19 Å. These may be compared with 1·10 in $N{\equiv}N$ and $1{\cdot}24 \pm 0{\cdot}05$ in $CH_3{-}N{=}N{-}CH_3$, and with 1·21 in $H{-}N{=}O$, 1·24 in NO_2^-, and 1·46 in $NH_2{-}OH$. From these data about 1·15 would be expected for a five-electron NN bond in which the nitrogen atoms, have a zero formal charge. But in N_2O the central atom carries a formal charge of $+1$ so the bond will be expected to be shorter. This is confirmed by the data for hydrazine and the hydrazinium ion (see section 4.4) and by the fact that the length of the five-electron bond in N_2^+, in which both atoms carry a formal charge of $+\frac{1}{2}$, is 1·12 Å. The three-electron NO bond in N_2O (1·19 Å) is also a little shorter than the three-electron bond in NO_2^- (1·24); the three-electron NO bond in CH_3NO_2 has a length of $1{\cdot}22 \pm 0{\cdot}02$ Å. The data are therefore reasonably consistent with the structure:

$$\overset{\times}{-}\mathrm{N}\overset{\circ}{=}\mathrm{N}\overset{\times}{-}\mathrm{O}\overset{\circ}{=}\,.$$

The ion NO_2^+ might also have the same six structures as were written for CO_2. The formal charges on the three atoms are the same as for CO_2 except that the formal charge on the central atom is always $+1$ (instead of zero). Since this formal charge is allowed on the nitrogen, it may be concluded that the electronic structure of NO_2^+ will be best represented by 4.IV. Providing therefore that the positive charge on the species can be stabilized, we may expect that NO_2^+ will be quite stable. This happens in certain crystals, and in solutions in sulphuric acid. The NO bond-length in NO_2^+ is 1·15 compared with 1·21 in HNO. This shortening in $\mathrm{N}\overset{\bullet}{\underset{\bullet}{-}}\mathrm{O}$ compared with N=O resembles that observed in CO_2 (see above).

The N_3^- ion will have, for the six structures listed for CO_2, the formal charges:

4.I	$-1, +1, -1$;	4.III	$0, +1, -2$;	4.V	$-1\frac{1}{2}, +1, -\frac{1}{2}$,
4.II	$-2, +1, 0$;	4.IV	$-1, +1, -1$;	4.VI	$-\frac{1}{2}, +1, -1\frac{1}{2}$.

None of these is really satisfactory, as, even with 4.I and 4.IV, the negative charges on the end nitrogen atoms are excessive. However, there must be some removal of this excessive negative charge by the central nitrogen atom which has a formal charge of $+1$, (cf. carbon monoxide). This stabilizes the ion a little but, nevertheless, as would be expected its stability is low. It does exist stably, and for an indefinite period at room temperature, in crystals such as that of sodium azide. Here the negative charges on the end nitrogen atoms are further stabilized by the field provided by the nearby positive charges.

Methyl azide can exist as a separate molecule though its stability is low. The structures analogous to 4.I to 4.VI are:

4.VII $\quad CH_3-\overset{|}{N}=N=N\langle$

4.VIII $\quad CH_3-\overset{|}{\underset{|}{N}}-N\equiv N-$

4.IX $\quad CH_3-N\equiv N-\overset{|}{\underset{|}{N}}-$

4.X $\quad CH_3-\overset{\times}{\underset{\times}{N}}\overset{\circ}{\underset{\circ}{-}}N\overset{\times}{\underset{\times}{-}}N\overset{\circ}{\underset{\circ}{-}}$

4.XI $\quad CH_3-\overset{\times}{\underset{|}{N}}\overset{\circ}{-}N\overset{\times}{=}N\overset{\circ}{-}$

4.XII $\quad CH_3-\overset{\times}{N}\overset{\circ}{=}N\overset{\times}{-}N\overset{\circ}{=}$

The formal charges for these are:

4.VII 0, +1, −1; 4.IX +1, +1, −2; 4.XI $-\frac{1}{2}, +1, -\frac{1}{2}$;
4.VIII −1, +1, 0; 4.X 0, +1, −1; 4.XII $+\frac{1}{2}, +1, -1\frac{1}{2}$.

Of these 4.XI is just allowable; each nitrogen atom carries a formal charge which is, according to Table 3, at the limit of what is allowable. It is therefore reasonable that it exists, but that its stability is low. The NN bond adjacent to the methyl has an order of $1\frac{1}{2}$ and the other an order of $2\frac{1}{2}$ in 4.XI. The observed bond lengths in CH_3NNN are $1{\cdot}24 \pm 0{\cdot}02$ Å and 1·10 Å respectively. Comparison with 1·10 in N≡N, $1{\cdot}24 \pm 0{\cdot}05$ in $CH_3N{=}NCH_3$ and 1·47 in $H_2N{-}NH_2$ shows that it is reasonable, having regard to the formal positive charge on the central atom, to assign to methyl azide the structure:

$$CH_3-\overset{\times}{\underset{|}{N}}\overset{\circ}{-}N\overset{\times}{\equiv}N\overset{\circ}{-}$$

For the NCO^- ion the formal charges on the three atoms are:

4.I −1, 0, 0; 4.III 0, 0, −1; 4.V $-1\frac{1}{2}, 0, +\frac{1}{2}$;
4.II −2, 0, +1; 4.IV −1, 0, 0; 4.VI $-\frac{1}{2}, 0, -\frac{1}{2}$.

The most satisfactory structure is therefore 4.VI which, besides having a formal charge distribution which is quite satisfactory, separates the electrons of one spin from those of the other. The CN bond has an order $2\frac{1}{2}$ in 4.VI and the CO bond an order of $1\frac{1}{2}$. The lengths of the two bonds are both 1·18 Å (Wells, see Appendix). The CN lengths may be compared with 1·16 Å in HC≡N and with 1·29 Å in $(CH_3)_2C{=}NOH$. The CO length may be compared with 1·16 in CO_2. In relation to the structure proposed the lengths are, therefore, not unreasonable and it seems that the structure:

$$-\overset{\times}{N}\overset{\circ}{=}C\overset{\times}{-}O\overset{\circ}{=}$$

is a satisfactory one to assign to it.

For the cyanamide ion, the structures 4.II, 4.III, 4.V and 4.VI will give to one or other of the nitrogen atoms a formal charge more negative than −1. Such structures cannot possibly be of any importance. Structures 4.I and 4.IV give to both nitrogen atoms formal charges of −1. Such a formal charge is most unsatisfactory. Moreover the adjacent carbon atom has a formal charge of zero, so that there will be little or no reduction of this high concentration of negative charge. The $CN_2^=$ ion is therefore unstable in solution; it only exists indefinitely when stabilized by positive ions in a crystal. Thus it is found in calcium cyanamide where it is stabilized by the strong field provided by the Ca^{++} ions.

In this section the six triatomic molecules and ions, in which there are sixteen valence-shell electrons, and which involve the atoms C, N and O, have been considered. There are, in fact, eighteen possible combinations of these three atoms. It is worth while seeing whether any of the others would be expected to exist.

Six of the eighteen have an oxygen atom at the centre. An oxygen atom in this position would have a formal charge of $+2$ for all six structures 4.I to 4.VI. Such a high formal charge is impossible so that no species having oxygen at the centre could possibly exist. The ions CCC^{4-} and CNC^{3-} also cannot possibly exist because every structure would have a charge of at least -2 on one of the carbon atoms; this is prohibitively large. The ions CCN^{3-} and CNN^{2-} are also excluded because every structure gives a formal charge of at least $-1\frac{1}{2}$ to one of the end atoms. Of the remaining eight, the six that exist have already been discussed. The other two are CNO^{-1} and CCO^{-2}. For the first the formal charges for the six structures are:

4.I	$-2, +1, 0$;	4.III	$-1, +1, -1$;	4.V	$-2\frac{1}{2}, +1, +\frac{1}{2}$,
4.II	$-3, +1, +1$;	4.IV	$-2, +1, 0$;	4.VI	$-1\frac{1}{2}, +1, -\frac{1}{2}$,

Of these, all are clearly excluded with possible exceptions of 4.III which might exist in a crystal stabilized by the presence of positive ions. However, the charge situation is very unsatisfactory, and much more unsatisfactory than that which can be achieved with the isomeric NCO^{-1} which was discussed earlier in this section. Consequently it is most unlikely that CNO^{-1} will ever be prepared, because it will be unstable relative to NCO^{-1}. The formal charges on CCO^{-2} are similar for the structures 4.I to 4.VI to those for CNO^{-1} except that the formal charge of $+1$ on the central atom is replaced throughout by zero. The only possible structure is

$$
\begin{array}{c} \qquad\qquad | \\ -C\equiv C-O- \\ \qquad\qquad | \end{array}
$$

for which there is a formal charge of -1 on both the end atoms. This could only be stabilized in a crystal in the field of a number of positive ions. It would, therefore, be expected that this would be extremely difficult to obtain and it is possible that an additional difficulty exists because it can decompose according to such reactions as:

$$CCO^{2-} \rightarrow C_2^{2-} + \tfrac{1}{2}O_2$$

and

$$CCO^{2-} \rightarrow O^{2-} + \text{carbon}.$$

The rules proposed do, therefore, account extremely well for which of these eighteen species will exist, and which will not. Moreover it accounts for the fact that CO_2 and N_2O will be stable, that the ions NO_2^+ and CNO^- will be quite stable, and that N_3^- and $CN_2^=$ will exist in certain circumstances but their stability will be low.

Cyanogen fluoride, FCN, is the only stable triatomic fluorine compound of the present type (i.e. with sixteen valence-shell electrons). The structure is certainly

$$—\overset{|}{\underset{|}{F}}—C\equiv N—$$

in which there is a zero formal charge on each atom. An ion such as FCC^{-1} will almost certainly be unstable relative to F^- and carbon, because the lattice energy of fluorides is high. The ion FCO^+ is not likely to be stable if it is supposed that the fluorine atom cannot assume a positive charge at all, and that oxygen does not readily assume a charge greater than $+\frac{1}{2}$. It would be most interesting to see whether any evidence for its existence in solution in 100% sulphuric acid could be obtained. The same applies to FNN^+ which might be formed from N_2F_2 in sulphuric acid. However, FCO^+ and FNN^+ would seem to be the only possibilities other than FCN, for sixteen electron triatomic species containing fluorine.

4.6 Other Molecules and Ions Related to CO_2

The CO bonds in CO_2, COS and COSe all have the length 1·16 Å. The CS bonds in CS_2, COS, CSSe and CSTe have the length 1·56. The CSe bonds in COSe and CSSe have the length 1·71. It is interesting that the lengths of the CO bond remains the same throughout, and that the same is true for the CS and CSe bonds. Pauling gives the following electronegativities: O, 3·5; S, 2·5; Se, 2·4; and Te 2·1. This is a big change, the difference between oxygen and tellurium being almost as big as that between carbon (2·5) and fluorine (4·0). If the stability of these molecules is to be regarded as a result of resonance among the three Lewis structures of the type of 4.I, 4.II and 4.III in section 4.5, it would have been expected that there would be some appreciable change in the relative contributions of 4.II and 4.III in the six different molecules referred to at the beginning of this section. On the other hand, if the stability is a consequence of a reduction in inter-electron repulsion, because of the adoption of the structure which for COS would be

$$\overset{\times}{\underset{\times}{-}}O\overset{\circ}{\underset{\circ}{-}}C\overset{\times}{\underset{\times}{-}}S\overset{\circ}{\underset{\circ}{-}}\ ,$$

then it would be expected that the electronic structures of all six molecules would be similar, and hence the observed constancy in the length of a given bond (CO, CS or CSe) is also to be expected.

The discussion in the last section led to the conclusion that, in the NCO^- ion, the electronic structure adopted placed a formal charge of $-\frac{1}{2}$ on each of the end atoms. Because the nitrogen atom is less ready to assume a negative charge than the oxygen atom, it is not surprising that, when the ion takes up a proton, it is attached to the nitrogen atom and HNCO is formed. The molecule HOCN is not known. Also the esters RNCO are known, but not the esters ROCN. In HNCO the NC bond length is 1·21, which is a little longer than that in NCO^- (1·18), while the CO bond length (1·17) may be a little shorter. This suggests that the structure H—N═C═O, in which each atom has a zero formal charge, may have some contributory importance.

4.7 Nitrogen Dioxide

In this chapter consideration has been given to triatomic species containing sixteen valence-shell electrons (CO_2, etc.) and those containing eighteen (O_3 and NO_2^-). The molecule NO_2 contains seventeen. According to the hypothesis proposed, the structure will be expected to be described most satisfactorily as a hybrid of

$$\overset{\times}{\underset{\times}{-}}O\overset{\circ}{\underset{\circ}{-}}\overset{\times}{N}\overset{\times}{-}\underset{|}{O}\overset{\circ}{-}\quad \text{and} \quad \overset{\circ}{-}\underset{|}{O}\overset{\times}{-}\overset{\times}{N}\overset{\circ}{\underset{\circ}{-}}O\overset{\times}{\underset{\times}{-}}\ .$$

In both these structures each atom has an octet of electrons made up of four of one spin, and four of the other. The bond length is 1·19 Å which is somewhat greater than that in NO_2^+ (1·15). This is to be expected because one bond is the same while the other contains one less electron.

In the above structures there are eight electrons of one spin (circles) and nine of the other (crosses). The first set will tend to make the three atoms lie on a straight line. The set of nine will tend to make the molecule bent, and to favour an ONO angle of about 120°. The ONO angle is, in fact, 134°. Because the bending force constant for a bent molecule (e.g. O_3) is greater than that for a linear one containing a triple and a single bond (e.g. HCN), it would be expected that the resultant angle would be nearer to 120° than to 180°. It is interesting that this bond angle of 134° in NO_2 is much larger than is usually found for 'bent' molecules, involving atoms of elements of the First Short Period (e.g. O_3) and hydrogen (e.g. H_2O). Consequently there is some significance in the fact that the above structure would lead to the expectation that the angle would be abnormally large; though not 180°.

The electronic structure explains the shape particularly well but, of course, there must be some strain involved for both sets of electrons, in that the nuclear arrangement does not really suit either set.

Nitrogen dioxide dimerizes readily to N_2O_4 for which the structure will be:

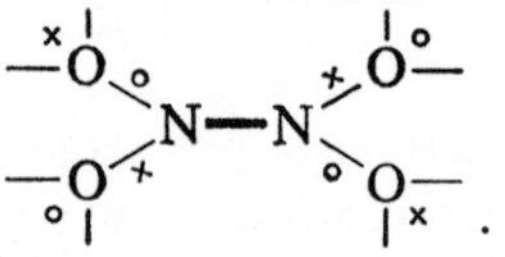

```
  x |          | o
 —O o        x O—
     \N——N/
 —O x        o O—
  o |          | x  .
```

This dimerization resembles that hypothetical one discussed earlier for nitric oxide, that is, both $2NO_2$ and N_2O_4 contain fourteen bonding electrons. However, in this system, the electronic structure of the dimer is such that the electrons of one spin have a different pattern from those of the other, so that, in both the monomer and the dimer, this factor causes a reduction in inter-electronic repulsion energy (in contrast to the nitric oxide system). Further, the electronic structure of N_2O_4 is such that both spin sets favour the same shape for the molecule. As has been said, the fact that this is not so for NO_2 means that there is some strain in the monomer. For these two reasons it is therefore not surprising that NO_2 does dimerize, whereas nitric oxide does not.

The heat of formation of N_2O_4 from NO_2 is only about 12 kcal/g mol. This is consistent with the fact that there is no increase in the number of bonding electrons on dimerization. According to the above formula the NN bond is an electron-pair bond but, because of the electron reorganization in the two NO_2 fragments as the NN bond length is increased, the 'rate' of the change in electronic energy with distance is small. As a result the NN bond will not only be weak energetically but also long. The planarity of N_2O_4 can be accounted for as a consequence of the set of three electrons binding one pair of oxygen atoms to a nitrogen atom tending to be staggered relative to the corresponding set of three on the other nitrogen atom (cf. the barrier in $CH_3.CH_3$).

Iso-electronic with N_2O_4 is $C_2O_4^{=}$, the oxalate ion. This ion does not dissociate at all under ordinary conditions to $2CO_2^{-}$, iso-electronic with NO_2. The reason for this is, that if the dissociation of

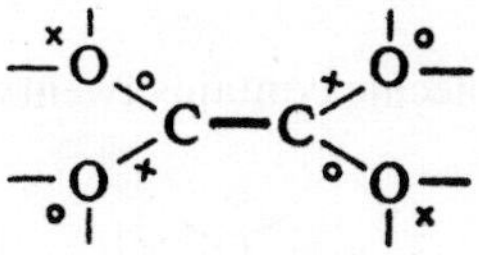

```
  ×|              |∘
 —O∘            ×,O—
     ╲C—C╱
   ╱×          ∘╲
 —O                O—
  ∘|              |×
```

is to occur without any decrease in the total number of bonding electrons (for it is only if this is so that dissociation will occur appreciably), the monomer must have the structure

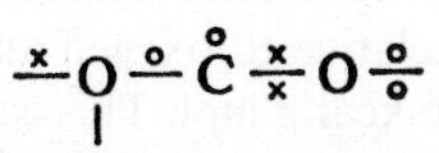

```
        ∘
 ×O ∘ C × O ∘
  |      ×
```

(along with its mirror image), in which the carbon atom, as well as one of the oxygen atoms, carries a formal charge of $-\frac{1}{2}$. This is not satisfactory energetically and consequently the dimeric oxalate ion $C_2O_4^{=}$ is strongly favoured; in $C_2O_4^{=}$ each of the four oxygen atoms carries a formal charge of $-\frac{1}{2}$. This is a most satisfactory charge distribution.

The ion CO_2^{-} has been observed by electron-spin resonance in a crystalline formate which had been subjected to high-energy radiation (Whiffen, *Proc. C.S.*, 1960). The unstable CO_2^{-} ions remained trapped in the solid. The E.S.R. spectrum is consistent with the structure described earlier.

4.8 The Ozonide Ion

So far in this chapter, triatomic molecules and ions containing sixteen, seventeen and eighteen valence-shell electrons have been considered. There is evidence that the substances NaO_3, KO_3 and CsO_3 exist and that they contain the O_3^{-} ion. This will have the electronic structure represented by

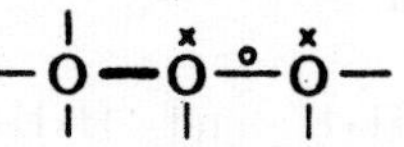

```
   |     ×   ∘  ×
 —O —— O ∘ O —
   |     |    |
```

(together with its mirror image). The formal charges are $-1, +\frac{1}{2}$ and $-\frac{1}{2}$ so the ion would be expected to be unstable.

The molecule ClO_2 contains the same number of valence-shell electrons as O_3^-. However, its structure is probably quite different because the chlorine atom is a member of the Second Short Period and its valence shell is not restricted to eight electrons. It will be discussed later (Chapter 8).

4.9 Oxygen Difluoride

The oxygen difluoride molecule contains twenty valence-shell electrons. The structure is

$$\text{F}\diagup\text{O}\diagdown\text{F}\,.$$

The pairs round the oxygen are spatially paired but unshared electrons on the fluorine atoms are not, since the two sets of three can be staggered relative to one another. Relative to oxygen and fluorine, F_2O is endothermic to the extent of 4·6 kcal/g mol. This can be understood because the number of shared electrons in $2F_2O$ is the same as in $2F_2+O_2$. However, in F_2O there are four pairs of electrons occupying the same spatial orbitals, whereas in F_2 there is only one and in O_2 there are none. The increase in energy on passing from $F_2+\frac{1}{2}O_2$ to F_2O is therefore to be ascribed, at any rate in part, to an increase in inter-electron repulsion energy.

4.10 The Reaction $H+H_2$

The study of the *para-ortho* hydrogen conversion has shown that the reaction

$$H+H_2 \rightarrow H_2+H$$

takes place with quite a small activation energy. If the hydrogen atom collides with the molecule so that the three nuclei are in a straight line, and there is some evidence that this is the easiest direction of approach for reaction to occur, the transition state will consist of three equally spaced nuclei. Calculations by H. C. Bowen (Oxford) have shown that the best simple way of describing the electronic structure of this transition state is as a hybrid of

$$\dot{\text{H}}\cdot\text{H}\cdot\text{H} \quad \text{and} \quad \text{H}\cdot\text{H}\cdot\dot{\text{H}}\,.$$

This is an important result as it suggests that, for reactions in other more complicated systems, such structures involving one-electron bonds may provide the best means of describing the structure of the transition states. In addition, wave functions based on such structures would then provide the best means of making calculations of the energy, etc., of such transition state complexes. This approach is pursued further to a small extent, and in a qualitative manner, in Chapter 6.

CHAPTER FIVE

More Examples in Simple Systems

5.1 Introduction

In this chapter some more examples will be presented for which the method of formulating structures that is proposed here seems to have certain advantages. Consideration will be limited mainly to species containing elements of the First Short Period only, for which the valence shell is limited to an octet of electrons; molecules containing elements of later periods will only be considered when there seems to be no reason for supposing that the atoms expand the valence shell beyond the octet (as in $ClNO_2$).

5.2 Formate Ion

The electronic system in the carboxylate ion is similar to that in the nitro-group. The formate ion will have the formula

$$-\underset{|}{\overset{\times}{O}}\overset{\circ}{-}\overset{H}{\overset{|}{C}}\overset{\times}{-}\underset{|}{\overset{\circ}{O}}- \ .$$

Other carboxylate ions, such as acetate will be similar. The CO bond length in the formate ion is $1{\cdot}26 \pm 0{\cdot}01$, depending a little on the nature of the positive ion in the crystal. This may be compared with 1·23 Å in $H_2C{=}O$. The OCO angle is in the neighbourhood of 125°. This somewhat large angle may be a consequence of the fact that both oxygen atoms carry a negative charge (both have formal charges of $-\frac{1}{2}$).

In the acid halides RCOX, where X represents a halogen atom, the CO bond length is about 1·17 Å; thus in HCOF it is $1{\cdot}19 \pm 0{\cdot}01$ and in CH_3COF, $1{\cdot}16 \pm 0{\cdot}02$. In COF_2, the length is $1{\cdot}17 \pm 0{\cdot}02$. This seems to imply that structures such as

$$\overset{\times}{-}O\overset{\circ}{=}\underset{H}{\underset{|}{C}} \times \underset{|}{\overset{|}{F}}\overset{\circ}{-}$$

have some importance (cf. 1·13 Å in CO). However, the CF bond is not lengthened relative to that in, say, CH_2F_2 so that the structure

$$\rangle\mathrm{O}=\underset{\mathrm{H}}{\underset{|}{\mathrm{C}}}-\overset{|}{\underset{|}{\mathrm{F}}}-$$

must also be important.

5.3 The Molecules C_nO_2

Carbon dioxide has been assigned the structure

$$\underset{\times}{\overset{\times}{-}}\mathrm{O}\underset{\circ}{\overset{\circ}{-}}\mathrm{C}\underset{\times}{\overset{\times}{-}}\mathrm{O}\underset{\circ}{\overset{\circ}{-}}\,.$$

On this basis C_2O_2 would be given the structure

$$\underset{\times}{\overset{\times}{-}}\mathrm{O}\underset{\circ}{\overset{\circ}{-}}\mathrm{C}\underset{\times}{\overset{\times}{-}}\mathrm{C}\underset{\circ}{\overset{\circ}{-}}\mathrm{O}\underset{\times}{\overset{\times}{-}}$$

and would be expected to be paramagnetic, if it existed, with two more electrons of one spin than of the other. Carbon suboxide would be given the structure

$$\underset{\times}{\overset{\times}{-}}\mathrm{O}\underset{\circ}{\overset{\circ}{-}}\mathrm{C}\underset{\times}{\overset{\times}{-}}\mathrm{C}\underset{\circ}{\overset{\circ}{-}}\mathrm{C}\underset{\times}{\overset{\times}{-}}\mathrm{O}\underset{\circ}{\overset{\circ}{-}}$$

and would be diamagnetic, having the same number of electrons of one spin as of the other.

From this formulation one concludes that the molecules C_nO_2 will be diamagnetic if n is odd, and paramagnetic if n is even. Molecular orbital theory leads to the same result, but simple valence-bond theory would assign to all structures of the type

$$\rangle\mathrm{O}=\mathrm{C}=\mathrm{C}=\mathrm{O}\langle \quad \text{and} \quad \rangle\mathrm{O}=\mathrm{C}=\mathrm{C}=\mathrm{C}=\mathrm{O}\langle\,,$$

and all would be diamagnetic.

In fact, of the species having $n = 1, 2$ and 3, only those with $n = 1$ and 3 are known (the diamagnetic members of the series). This is probably not a consequence of their diamagnetism, but C_2O_2 is unlikely to exist because it will split up into 2CO. Such a dissociation is likely to be exothermic because triple bonds between atoms of elements in the First Short Period are very strong. Carbon suboxide cannot split up in this way, but would have to form initially $2CO+C$ which would contain twelve bonding-electrons, as against sixteen in the original C_3O_2.

This method therefore accounts for the existence of CO_2 and C_3O_2, and the non-existence of C_2O_2 (as would the valence-bond method using Lewis structures). However, it is interesting that it agrees with the molecular orbital method regarding the expected magnetism, which differs from the formulation using Lewis structures.

The bond lengths in C_3O_2 are: CC, $1{\cdot}28 \pm 0{\cdot}03$, and CO, $1{\cdot}19 \pm 0{\cdot}03$. The CC bond is shorter than the normal CC double-bond in C_2H_4 (1·33 Å) which is similar to what was found for N$\div$O and C$\div$O (see last chapter). The CO bond is certainly shorter than the normal CO double-bond in H_2CO. However, the accuracy of the data leaves uncertain whether it has the same length as that in CO_2 (1·16) as it would be expected to have.

5.4 Nitrosyl Halides and other Nitroso-compounds

In this section the electronic structures of molecules having the general formula ANO will be considered, where A is monovalent and may be a halogen atom (X), a hydrogen atom (H), or an alkyl or aryl radical (R) (see Linnett and Rosenberg, *Tetrahedron*, 1963).

Five reasonable electronic structures are possible for XNO:

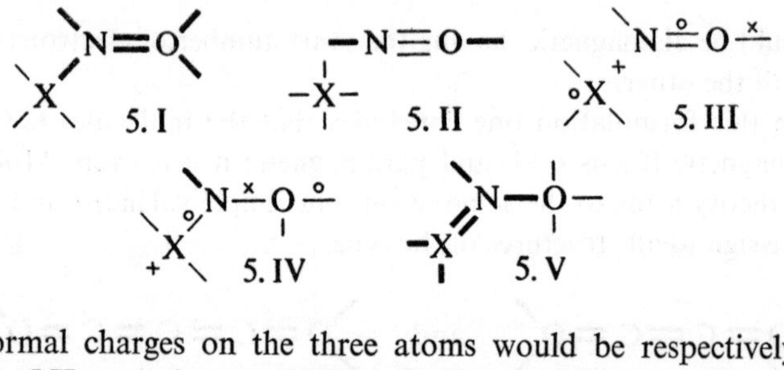

5.I 5.II 5.III

5.IV 5.V

The formal charges on the three atoms would be respectively: 5.I: 0, 0, 0; 5.II: −1, 0, +1; 5.III: $-\frac{1}{2}$, 0, $+\frac{1}{2}$; 5.IV: $+\frac{1}{2}$, 0, $-\frac{1}{2}$; 5.V: +1, 0, −1. If X were fluorine structures 5.IV and 5.V would be excluded (see Table 3), and they would probably have low probability relative to the others for any other halogen. Structure 5.II will also be expected to have low probability relative to 5.I and 5.III, because of the formal charge of +1 on the oxygen atom. With HNO and RNO, structures such as 5.IV and 5.V can also be excluded; 5.II can be eliminated as well, because a structure containing H^- or CH_3^- is not likely to be important. Therefore, for all the species (XNO, HNO and RNO), consideration can be limited to 5.I and 5.III.

The advantage of 5.I is that there are formal charges of zero on each of the three centres (A, N and O). The disadvantage of 5.I is that there are six 'coincident' pairs of electrons, where the word 'coincident' is used to imply that there are two in the same spatial orbital (i.e. shared or unshared). The disadvantage of 5.III is that there are formal charges of $-\frac{1}{2}$ and $+\frac{1}{2}$ on A and O respectively. The advantage of 5.III is that, all twelve electrons associated with the nitrogen and oxygen atoms are in different orbitals, and so inter-electron repulsion is reduced. If, therefore, the atom or group A can assume a negative charge without a great increase of energy, the favoured structure will be 5.III so that the inter-electron repulsion energy is reduced. If, on the other hand, it is prohibitive energetically for A to assume a negative charge then the structure must be 5.I. Consequently if A is X (F, Cl, Br) the structure expected will be 5.III, but if A is H, CH_3, C_6H_5, etc., the structures expected will be 5.I. The structural data for these compounds support these conclusions.

In FNO, ClNO and BrNO, the NX bonds are all much longer than the normal single bonds: FN, 1·52 Å (cf. 1·37 in NF_3); ClN, 1·95 (cf. 1·76 in $NHCl_2$ and 1·77 in NH_2Cl); BrN, 2·14 (cf. 1·84, sum of Pauling's single-bond radii). The NO bond lengths in the three molecules are 1·13, 1·14 and 1·15 (cf. 1·15 in NO and 1·06 in NO^+). Contrasting with the above, the NO bond length in HNO is 1·21. The Schomaker–Stevenson formula, with the numerical coefficients listed in Pauling's book, leads to an expected value for the NO double bond of 1·20. The NH bond length is 1·06 as compared with 1·02 in NH_3.

The vibration frequencies bring out even more clearly the difference between XNO on the one hand and HNO and RNO on the other. The NO vibration frequencies in FNO, ClNO and BrNO are 1844, 1801 and 1799 cm^{-1} respectively (cf. 1876 cm^{-1} in NO). The corresponding frequency in HNO is 1562 cm^{-1}, and those in CH_3NO and $C_6H_{11}NO$ 1564 and 1558 cm^{-1} respectively. The NO stretching frequency in NO^+, which contains a triple bond, is about 2300 cm^{-1}. The NH frequency in HNO is 3396 cm^{-1} as compared with the two NH stretching frequencies of 3336 and 3414 cm^{-1} in NH_3. These data undoubtedly support the following formulae:

$\mathrm{X{-}N{=}O}$ $\mathrm{H{-}N{=}O}$ $\mathrm{R{-}N{=}O}$.

Pauling accounts for the long NX and short NO bonds in the nitrosyl halides by supposing that their structures can be described best by a hybrid of 5.I and 5.II (5.V also having some slight importance). The present explanation has two advantages compared with this. It provides a natural explanation of why the NO bond in the nitrosyl halides is very similar to that in nitric oxide itself. It also explains why the NO bonds in the three halides are so similar to one another. If resonance between 5.I and 5.II were important, then bigger variation would have been expected as the change in electronegativity on going from F (4·0) to Br (2·8) (cf. O, 3·5), is large, and a considerable change in the proportion of the two forms would have been expected. The smallish changes observed are probably due to electrostatic effects. For example the NO frequencies of 1844 and 1799 in FNO and BrNO may be compared with those of 1595 and 1564 in CF_3NO and CH_3NO. This shows the increase in frequency produced by replacing hydrogen by electronegative fluorine atoms.

5.5 Dimerization of Nitroso-compounds

Organic nitroso-compounds dimerize readily. That is 2RNO forms $(RNO)_2$, R being either alkyl or aryl. On the other hand, FNO, ClNO and BrNO do not dimerize. This is a somewhat startling observation, because the lengths of the NX bonds and the NO characteristic frequencies show that the structures of the XNO compounds are, in terms of conventional structures, abnormal or, at least, unexpected; whereas the structural data for the organic nitroso-compounds, RNO, shows that they have normal Lewis-structures containing an ordinary single and an ordinary double bond, which might have been expected to be stable. That is, the apparently normal molecules dimerize, while the apparently abnormal ones do not. In the terms of the structures proposed here, the structures involving bonds containing an odd number of electrons are stable; on the other hand, those structures made up of coincident pairs suffer from an increase in the inter-electron repulsion energy, and so their stability is lower.

On the hypothesis being proposed in this book, these results are the expected ones. The molecules of the organic nitroso-compounds suffer from a high value of the inter-electron repulsion energy because twelve electrons in the NO system occupy six spatial orbitals in pairs. If the electron repulsion energy can be reduced by dimerization, then there is a reason for that process to take place. Possible formulae for the dimer are 5.VI, 5.VII, 5.VIII and 5.IX, together, of course, with the mirror images of 5.VII and 5.VIII. The formal charges and number of close electron pairs (excluding those within the radical R) are listed in Table 5. This shows that 5.VI will not be expected to make a major contribution, because of both the charge distribution and the number of close pairs. Structure 5.VII has a better charge distribution, but inter-electron repulsion will be large because of the number of close pairs. Of the remaining two structures, 5.IX would be expected to be much preferred. However, there are two structures of the type of 5.VIII (itself and its mirror image). We may, therefore, expect that the NN bond will be

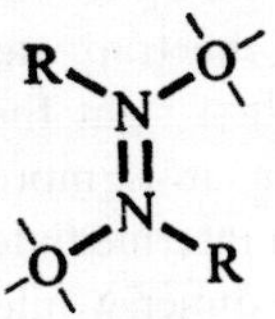

5.VI 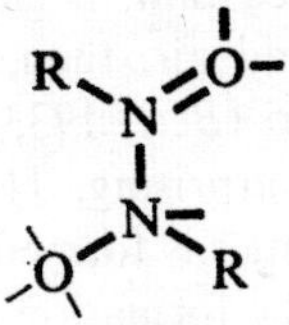 5.VII 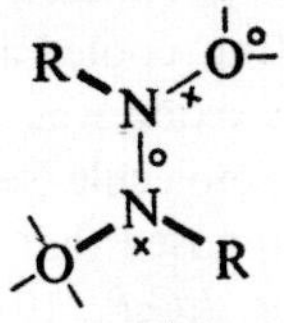 5.VIII 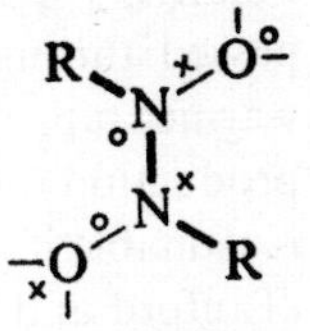 5.IX

TABLE 5

Formal charges

	O	N	N	O	No of close pairs
5.VI	−1	+1	+1	−1	6
5.VII	0	+1	0	−1	9
5.VIII	$-\frac{1}{2}$	+1	$+\frac{1}{2}$	−1	3
5.IX	$-\frac{1}{2}$	$+\frac{1}{2}$	$+\frac{1}{2}$	$-\frac{1}{2}$	3

stronger and shorter than a single bond and that the order of the NO bond will be about $1\frac{1}{2}$. The NN bond length in the dimer of BrC_6H_4NO is 1·31, compared with 1·47 in $NH_2—NH_2$ but 1·40 in $\overset{+}{N}H_3—\overset{+}{N}H_3$ and with 1·24 in $CH_3—N{=}N.CH_3$. The NO bond length is 1·35 compared with 1·21 in HN=O and 1·46 in $NH_2—OH$.

There is one advantage that 5.VIII has relative to 5.IX. In 5.IX the electrons of different spins favour different shapes. One set favours a planar arrangement at one nitrogen, and a non-planar arrangement at the other; the other set favours the reverse pattern. On the other hand, with 5.VIII, both sets favour a planar arrangement at one nitrogen (upper one in 5.VIII); at the other, however, one set favours a non-planar arrangement (crosses) while the other set (circles) favours a planar arrangement. This difference will somewhat favour the two structures of type 5.VIII relative to 5.IX. So perhaps the best description may well be something like an equal contribution from (*a*) the two structures of type 5.VIII, and (*b*) structure 5.IX. The shape of the molecule is consistent with this assessment.

The molecule HNO has been observed spectroscopically but is unstable and has a short life (Dalby, *Can. J. of P.*, 1958; Cashion and Polanyi, *J.C.P.*, 1959). Harteck showed that, if gas containing it was passed through a trap cooled in liquid air, then, when the trap was warmed up, nitrous oxide was formed (*Ber.*, 1933). At first sight the production of this molecule seems surprising. However, it is more reasonable if it is supposed that the dimer is formed as an intermediate (Tanford and Taylor, *J.C.P.*, 1944). The formation of the dimer would be followed by the migration of hydrogen atoms and, on this hypothesis, the formation of N_2O and H_2O can be readily understood.

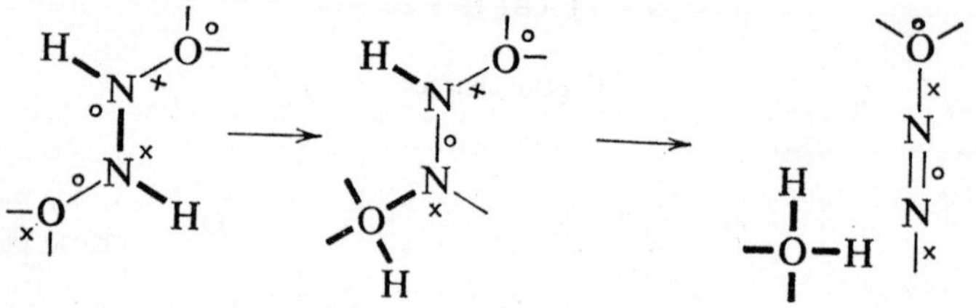

This would not be expected to happen with the aryl compounds, as a bulky aryl group would not migrate as readily as a hydrogen atom.

5.6 Nitryl Chloride

In nitryl chloride, NO_2Cl, the NO bond length is 1·20 Å and the ONO angle 130½° (Millen and Sinnott, *J.C.S.*, 1958). However, more surprisingly, the NCl bond length is 1·84 Å, which is much less than that in ClNO (1·95 Å), but a little greater than that in NH_2Cl (1·77 Å). There are three possible structures which separate the electrons of one spin effectively from those of the other. They are:

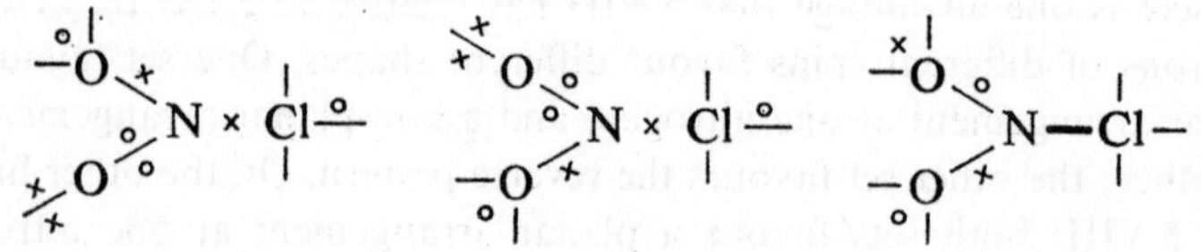

5.X   5.XI   5.XII

Of these, 5.X and 5.XI place formal charges of $-\frac{1}{2}$ on one of the oxygen atoms and the chlorine atom, while 5.XII places formal charges of $-\frac{1}{2}$ on the two oxygen atoms. All structures place a formal charge of $+1$ on the central nitrogen atom.

Structure 5.XII has the slight disadvantage that there is one pair of electrons occupying the same bonding orbital. However, 5.X and 5.XI suffer from the rather greater disadvantage that one set of electrons favour ONO being linear while the other set favour it being non-linear. It is, therefore, to be expected that the three structures will be about equally important, with 5.XII being perhaps a little more important than the other two. The NCl bond length supports this conclusion. The ONO angle is greater than that in *p*-dinitrobenzene (124°) but not as great as that in NO_2 (134°), which is consistent with the above interpretation. This also accounts for the fact that the NO bond is a little shorter than that in the ordinary nitro-group (1·22 Å).

It is interesting that, in ClNO, separation of the electrons of one spin-set from those of the other can only be achieved by complete involvement of the NCl bond and consequently it is very long. In NO_2Cl this separation can be achieved both by involving the NCl bond, and also without involving it. As a result, the NCl bond is shorter, but not as short as in NH_2Cl.

The structure of FNO_2 is still rather doubtful. However, it can be said, with complete certainty, that the FN bond is not abnormally long and so does not resemble the NF bond in FNO (length 1·52). The length is said to be 1·35 (the possible error is uncertain); that in NF_3 is $1{\cdot}37 \pm 0{\cdot}02$. Again the distinction between the NX bonds in XNO and XNO_2 is brought out clearly.

5.7 Dioxygen Difluoride

The arrangement of the atoms in the molecule of this compound is FOOF, which is what is to be expected. But otherwise, the structure is perhaps unexpected (Jackson, *J.C.S.*, 1962). The O—O bond length is 1·22 Å, which is almost the same as that in O_2 (1·21), and much smaller than that in HOOH (1.48). The length of the OF bond is 1·58 Å (cf. 1·41 in OF_2). This long OF bond is reminiscent of the long NF bond in FNO (1·52 as against 1·37 in NF_3). In both cases the length is about 10% greater than that of a normal single bond. Ten reasonable structures can be formulated for F_2O_2. They are 5.XIII, 5.XIV and its mirror image; 5.XV, 5.XVI and its mirror image; 5.XVII, 5.XVIII, 5.XIX and its mirror image.

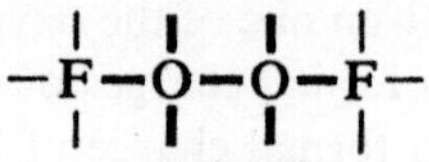

5. XIII 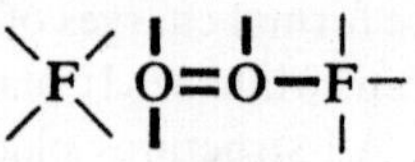　　5. XIV 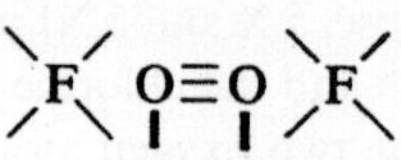　　5. XV

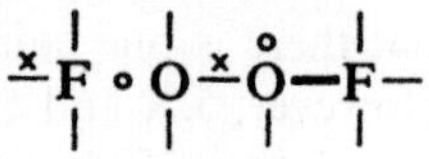

5. XVI 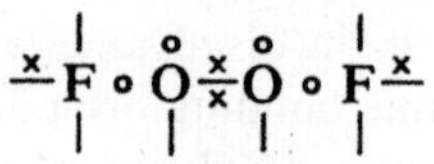　　5. XVII 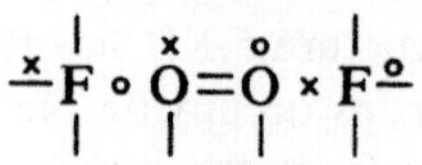　　5. XVIII

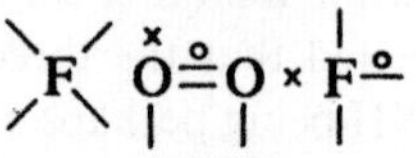

5. XIX

The formal charges on the atoms F, O, O, F in the structures 5.XIII to 5.XIX are listed in Table 6. This table also lists the number of electron pairs which are occupying the same bond or lone-pair orbitals.

TABLE 6

Structure	Formal charges on:				Number of close pairs
	F	O	O	F	
5.XIII	0	0	0	0	7
5.XIV	−1	0	+1	0	6
5.XV	−1	+1	+1	−1	2
5.XVI	$-\frac{1}{2}$	0	$+\frac{1}{2}$	0	1
5.XVII	$-\frac{1}{2}$	$+\frac{1}{2}$	$+\frac{1}{2}$	$-\frac{1}{2}$	0
5.XVIII	$-\frac{1}{2}$	$+\frac{1}{2}$	$+\frac{1}{2}$	$-\frac{1}{2}$	0
5.XIX	−1	$+\frac{1}{2}$	+1	$-\frac{1}{2}$	0

Of these, 5.XIV, 5.XV and 5.XIX are probably of low importance because of the existence of a formal charge of +1 on at least one oxygen atom. Structure 5.XIII is likely to be unimportant, because of the high value of the inter-electron repulsion energy as a result of the presence of seven close pairs. This leaves 5.XVI and its mirror image, 5.XVII and 5.XVIII. Of these, 5.XVI has one close pair of electrons which will tend to reduce its importance.

Another feature of the structure of FOOF is that the plane of one FOO makes an angle of 87½° with the plane of the other FOO (the FOO angle itself is 109½°). In 5.XVIII, the two electrons of one spin in the OO bond can be separated from the two electrons of the other spin in that bond, if the two sets tend to keep in planes at right angles to one another. Because of the need to maintain the tetrahedral arrangement of both the spin sets, this would mean that the two FOO planes would be at right angles to one another; the experimental value is close to 90°.

The two structures, 5.XVI and its mirror image, are favoured relative to 5.XVII and 5.XVIII by the fact that only two atoms carry formal charges of ½, as opposed to four for 5.XVII and 5.XVIII. On the other hand, 5.XVII and 5.XVIII are favoured because they contain no close pairs. This tends to suggest that all four structures should be given about equal weight. If this were the case, the O—O bond would be expected to have a length of 1·24 Å (between 1·28 in O_2^- and 1·21 in O_2). The length of 1·22, however, implies that 5.XVII and 5.XVIII are more important than 5.XVI and its mirror image. This structure is consistent with the long OF bonds and the angle between the OF planes, and also with the observation that the barrier restricting the rotation of one OF relative to the other is high; this barrier is provided by 5.XVII.

Structures 5.XVI and 5.XVII are of importance in dioxygen difluoride, because the fluorine atom can readily assume a negative charge. This is not possible with HOOH and, consequently, the molecule of hydrogen peroxide has the structure 5.XVIII; all the other nine place some negative charge on the hydrogen, and the energy that would be involved in this renders them unimportant. The contrast between HOOH and FOOF is therefore similar to that between HNO and FNO.

5.8 Dinitrogen Difluoride

Similar considerations to those of the last section suggest that the following structures should be considered for FNNF:

−F−N=N−F− ⁻°F × N=N−F− ⁻°F × N≡N ∘ F⁻ˣ .

5.XX   5.XXI   5.XXII

There is also the mirror image of 5.XXI. The Lewis structure, 5.XX, places zero formal charges on all four atoms, whereas for 5.XXI and

5.XXII the formal charges are $-\frac{1}{2}$, 0, $+\frac{1}{2}$, 0, and $-\frac{1}{2}$, $+\frac{1}{2}$, $+\frac{1}{2}$, $-\frac{1}{2}$ respectively. Structure 5.XX places six pairs of electrons in the same spatial orbitals, so that inter-electron repulsion would be expected to be high. Structure 5.XXI has only one pair of electrons in the same orbital so that inter-electron repulsion will be less than in 5.XXI. On the other hand, at one nitrogen atom (the right-hand one) the electrons of one spin favour a different shape from those of the other spin. Structure 5.XXII favours a linear shape for the whole molecule, and the pattern of the tetrahedra does not allow the electrons of one spin to be separated from those of the other. It is probable that the three important structures will be 5.XX, 5.XXI and its mirror image. The molecule would therefore be expected to be planar, and this is found experimentally. The NF bond would be expected to be a little longer than that in NF_3, but the order in N_2F_2 would be expected to differ from one by a smaller amount than for the OF bond in O_2F_2. The lengths are N_2F_2, $1{\cdot}44 \pm 0{\cdot}04$; NF_3, $1{\cdot}371$. The percentage increase is about 5%. In O_2F_2 this was a 12% increase with respect to the bond in OF_2. The NN bond length is $1{\cdot}25 \pm 0{\cdot}02$, compared with $1{\cdot}24 \pm 0{\cdot}05$ in $(CH_3)_2N_2$. There is therefore no sign of the NN bond being shorter in $(CH_3)_2N_2$ as would have been expected. However, the data are poor.

The two features of the structure of N_2F_2 that are certain can therefore be understood. These are the planarity and the slight increase in the NF bond length compared with NF_3.

5.9 Peroxy-radicals

Studies of the hydrogen–oxygen reaction have shown that the radical HO_2 is an important participant in the sequence of processes that take place. The observations show, in addition, that HO_2 is less reactive in the temperature range 500°–600° C than OH.

The structure of HO_2 is expected to be

$$H-\underset{|}{\overset{\times}{O}}\overset{\circ}{-}\underset{|}{\overset{\times}{O}}- \, .$$

The formal charges of $+\frac{1}{2}$ and $-\frac{1}{2}$ on the two oxygen atoms are acceptable energetically. In HO_2, as written above, there are two and a half bonds. Two radicals might react together to give H_2 and $2O_2$ or to give $H_2O_2 + O_2$, but, in either case, there is no increase in the number of bonds since both the above systems contain five bonds. In $2HO_2$ there are two pairs of electrons occupying the same orbital whereas in H_2+2O_2 there is only one close pair. Also in H_2+2O_2 the formal charges on the atoms are all zero. Therefore, both because of the reduction in inter-electron repulsion and because of the elimination of the formal charges, (H_2+2O_2) will be expected to be markedly more stable than $2HO_2$. Consequently we shall not anticipate that it will be possible to isolate HO_2. On the other hand OH can react with another OH, or with H, to form an entirely new bond so that the number of bonding electrons is increased. Therefore OH would be expected to be more reactive than HO_2, as is observed.

When methyl radicals, formed by illuminating methyl iodide with ultra-violet light, react with oxygen, CH_3O_2 is formed first. The experimental evidence indicates that this radical has a long life. The radical CH_3O_2 will have a structure similar to that given above for HO_2 and the explanation of its relatively low reactivity is similar.

5.10 Carbonate and Nitrate

The structure of these two ions will be expected to be described by a combination of three structures of the type

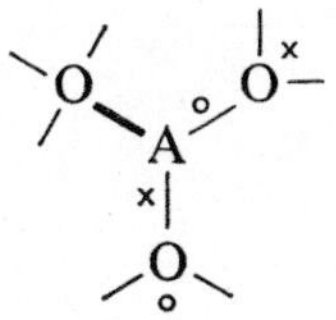

when A = C in the carbonate and N in the nitrate. The formal charges on the three oxygen atoms are -1, $-\frac{1}{2}$ and $-\frac{1}{2}$ in both ions. In the carbonate the formal charge on the central atom is zero, and in the nitrate $+1$.

The carbonate ion readily takes up a proton in aqueous solution to give

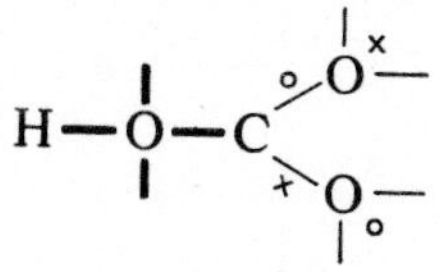

in which the formal charges on the oxygen atoms are 0, $-\frac{1}{2}$ and $-\frac{1}{2}$. The attachment of the proton has therefore eliminated the formal charge of -1 on the one oxygen atom in $CO_3^=$. Since this formal charge must be produced when HCO_3^- loses a proton, HCO_3^- is a very weak acid. On the

CHAPTER SIX

Some Organic Molecules and Reactions

6.1 Introduction

The object of this chapter is to describe the application of the ideas presented in this book to a number of organic molecules and ions, and also to several organic reaction mechanisms. A book of this kind would be incomplete if a consideration of the benzene molecule were not included. This chapter therefore starts with this topic. A short discussion is also given of the structure of some compounds containing nitrogen and oxygen (e.g. furoxan); this is related to the discussion of nitroso compounds (section 5.4). There are further sections on triphenylmethane dyes, and cyanine dyes; and also on the mechanism of the bromination of butadiene, and of the Claisen condensation.

6.2 Benzene

The benzene molecule is too complicated for a complete theoretical treatment of all the thirty valence-shell electrons. Consequently attention has always been focused on the six electrons which, in the molecular orbital terminology, form the π-system. This is the group which has also been called the *aromatic sextet*. The remaining twenty-four electrons are regarded as forming twelve single bonds of the σ-system, and only their mean effect is considered. The σ-system is

H H

H– –H .

H H

The six electrons of the π-system may be regarded, in simple terms, as participating in a ring system, and the considerations of section 1.6 apply. In that case it was found that the three electrons of one spin tended to be disposed at 120° to one another, and those of the other spin tended to be disposed similarly. As far as the effects of spin correlation were concerned, the electrons of one spin had a slight tendency to be disposed in coincidence with those of the other spin; that is, the highest probability was for an arrangement in which three pairs were at 120° to one another. The effect of charge correlation, on the other hand, will favour the two spin-sets being staggered relative to one another, so that the six electrons are spaced at intervals of 60° round the ring. Charge and spin correlation will, of course, favour the same disposition within each spin-set. Therefore, if spin correlation is the more important, the total wave function will be close to a mixture of wave functions corresponding to 6.I and 6.II.

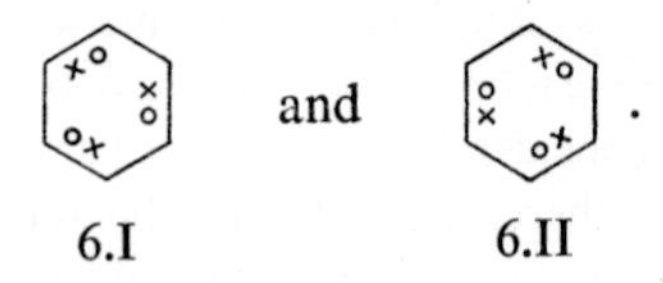

6.I 6.II

These are the two Kekulé structures, and the molecular orbital description links with the Pauling resonance formulation in this way; (it is true that, as the wave functions are usually written, the valence-bond formulation places a greater restriction on the electrons than does the M.O. formulation; however, this does not affect the connection in principle). On the other hand, if the effects of charge repulsion are more important than the effects of spin correlation between the two spin-sets, the molecular orbital formulation may be modified to one depicted by

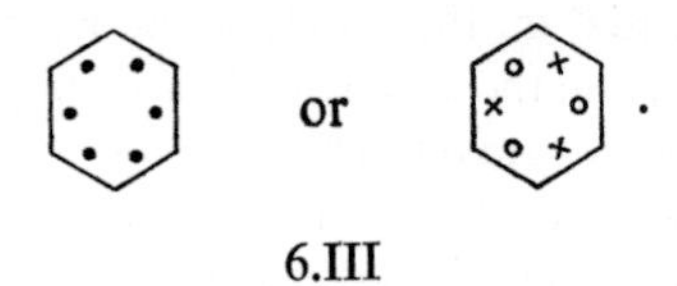

6.III

It is proposed here that this is the most satisfactory way of formulating a description of the benzene molecule in terms that localize the distribution of the electrons. It will reduce inter-electron repulsion by separating the electrons of one spin from those of the other, whereas the valence bond description (resonance between two Kekulé forms) will, if anything, tend to enhance inter-electron repulsion, though the extent to which this happens will depend on the way in which the wave functions representing the two Kekulé formulae are chosen.

P. B. Empedocles (Oxford) has made calculations of the energy corresponding to a wave function based on the structure 6.III. He finds that the electronic energy calculated is 69 kcal/g mol lower than that calculated using a Hückel type molecular orbital function (without any configuration interaction). The reduction in the calculated energy must result from a reduction in the inter-electron repulsion energy.

The main conclusions to be drawn from the calculation are that, if a localized description of the benzene molecule is to be used, 6.III is probably the best; and also that this description possesses some advantages over the molecular orbital description.

Empirically, the so-called resonance energy has been found to be about 36 kcal/g mol. This measures the amount by which the true energy of the molecule is less than that calculated for one of the Kekulé forms. On the present hypothesis this is due to a reduction in inter-electron repulsion energy. In the ring system there are, for 6.I or 6.II, nine pairs of electrons occupying the same orbitals; in 6.III there are none (in both cases the CH bonds are excluded). The reduction per electron pair is therefore about 4 kcal. This is essentially the same as the figure that was found for CO_2; it is less than that found for O_2 (6 kcal per electron pair) but, as has been suggested earlier, the effect is likely to be bigger for oxygen than for carbon since the 'volume' of the oxygen orbitals will be less than those of carbon, because of the difference between the nuclear charges.

In the remainder of this book, therefore, the benzene ring will be depicted as 6.III.

6.3 Acid Strength of Nitrophenols

This section provides an example of the way in which this hypothesis may be used to account for the effect of substituents on the properties of aromatic compounds.

The anion from phenol is:

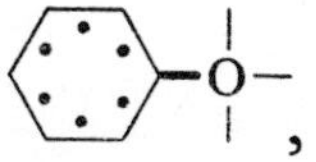

,

in which there is a formal charge of −1 on the oxygen atom. With *para*-nitrophenol, additional structures are possible for the anion; that is

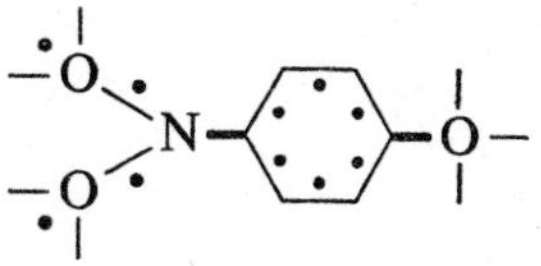

6.IV

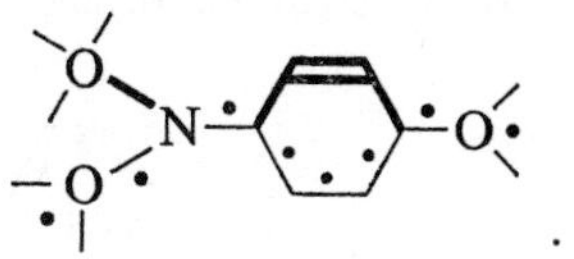

6.V

.

In addition to 6.IV there are four of the type of 6.V. All five structures place formal charges of $-\frac{1}{2}$, $-\frac{1}{2}$ and -1 on the three oxygen atoms, but they do this in various ways. If the total wave function is a combination of wave functions corresponding to these five structures, there will be five squared-terms (Ψ_I^2) and twenty cross-terms ($\Psi_I \Psi_{II}$) in the square of the total function which measures the electron distribution. Several of the cross terms will involve a charge distribution which will amount to $-\frac{1}{2}$, $-\frac{3}{4}$, $-\frac{3}{4}$. Therefore the presence of the nitro-group means that the charge, all of which in phenol is located normally on the oxygen atom, is spread among several atoms. Consequently *para*-nitrophenol more readily loses a proton; that is, it is a stronger acid. In fact, the dissociation constant is about 1000 times as big. With *ortho*-nitrophenol the dissociation constant is also increased by about this factor. On the other hand, with *meta*-nitrophenol, for which such structures are impossible, the increase is 40-fold, and this is presumably an electrostatic effect of the formal positive charge on the nitrogen atom. With 2,4-dinitrophenol and 2,6-dinitrophenol, the dissociation constant is a million times as big as that of phenol, and in 2,4,6-trinitrophenol it is about a thousand million times as big. However, in 2,5- and 3,4-dinitrophenol, in which one of the nitro groups is *meta* to the hydroxyl group, the increase in the dissociation constant is about 40,000-fold (see Pauling, *Nature of the Chemical Bond*).

6.4 Attack on Aromatic Systems

The most common type of reagent that attacks an aromatic system is an electrophilic one, and a typical example of such a reagent is the nitronium ion, NO_2^+, which is the active agent in solutions of nitric acid in sulphuric acid.

The formula of the nitronium ion, which was discussed in section 4.5, is

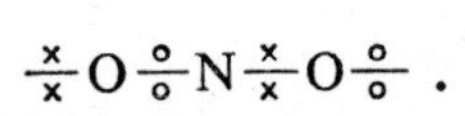

$$\frac{\times}{\times}O\frac{\circ}{\circ}N\frac{\times}{\times}O\frac{\circ}{\circ}\ .$$

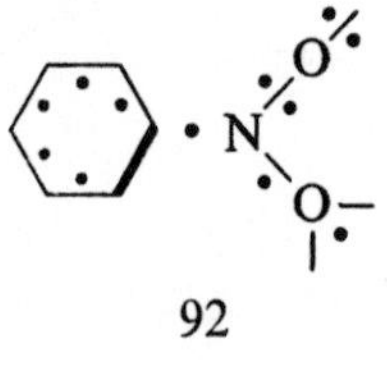

The nitrogen atom carries a formal charge of $+1$, those on the oxygen being zero. Therefore the N-atom will be the primary electrophilic atom, and initially there will be formed (and there are several other similar structures). There is now a formal charge of $+\frac{1}{2}$ on the *ortho* carbon atom (but in the equivalent structures this will be on the *ortho* or the *para* atoms). Next we may suppose the electronic structure passes over to

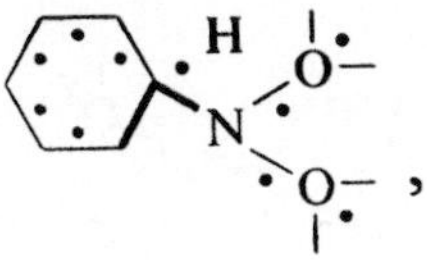

and then finally to

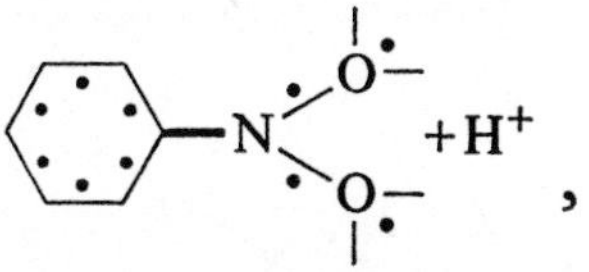

$+H^+$,

the proton being taken up by a base. In the whole succession of structures, the number of electrons in bonds remains constant so that the greater energy of the intermediate structures is due to the increase associated with the assumption by one of the atoms in the ring of a formal positive charge of $+\frac{1}{2}$. This can be made unnecessary if there is a substituent of a suitable kind at a suitable place on the benzene ring. Thus with phenol the first intermediate structure will be replaced by

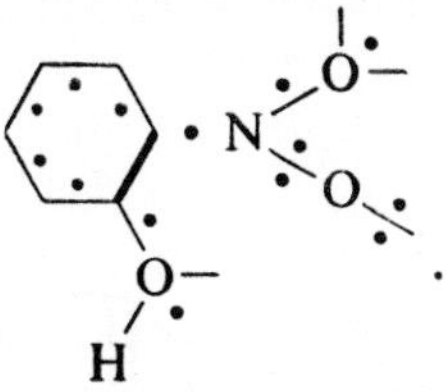

In this intermediate species the formal charge of $+\frac{1}{2}$ is located on the oxygen atom instead of the carbon. Because the oxygen atom assumes a positive charge of $+\frac{1}{2}$ much more readily than does the carbon, this intermediate has a much lower energy than the intermediate formed with benzene. Consequently the attack will be much more rapid than it is on benzene. However, the formal charge of $+\frac{1}{2}$ can only be transferred to the oxygen of the hydroxyl group if the NO_2^+ ion attacks in the *ortho* or *para* positions relative to that group. Therefore, attack occurs more rapidly in those positions.

If a nitro-group is attached to the benzene ring, the nitrogen atom carrying a formal positive charge of +1, which is directly attached to the ring, will draw electrons towards it to some extent. This can be represented by describing the system in terms of the main structure

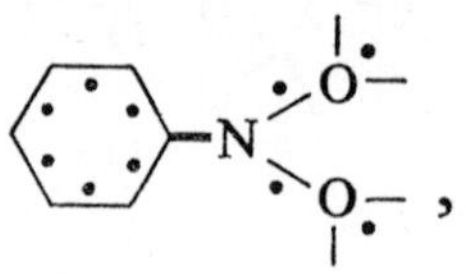

together with small contributions from several such as

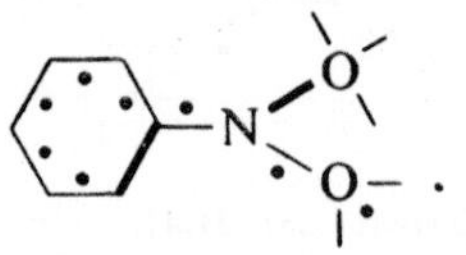

The above structure leaves a formal positive charge of $+\frac{1}{2}$ on the *ortho* position; it may also be on the *para* carbon atom. Consequently, attack by the electrophilic nitronium ion will be particularly 'discouraged' in the *ortho* and *para* positions.

In the case of thiophene, attack could take place either at the α- or the β-positions; the intermediate species in the two cases would be

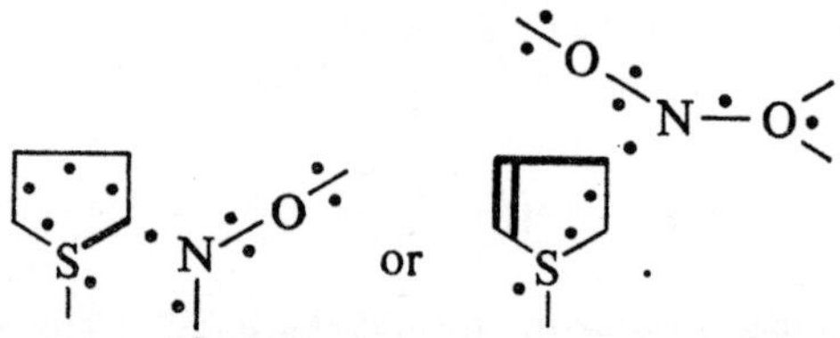

or

The first of these separates electrons to a greater extent than does the second. Therefore the energy of the first intermediate structure will be less than that of the second, and attack would therefore be expected to occur in the α-position; this is found experimentally.

Aromatic systems can also be attacked by anionoid reagents, an example of which is the diphenylamide ion $N(C_6H_5)_2^-$, obtainable as the potassium salt. This will attack nitrobenzene in the *para* position. The intermediate structure will be expected to be

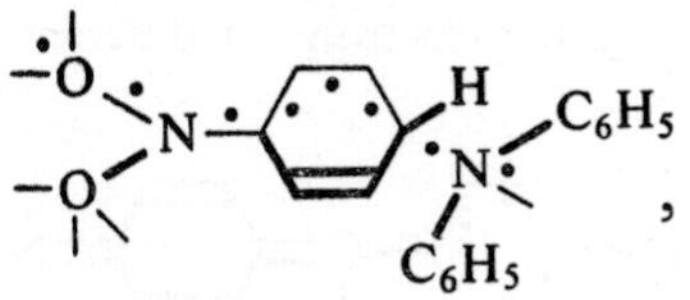

this will pass to

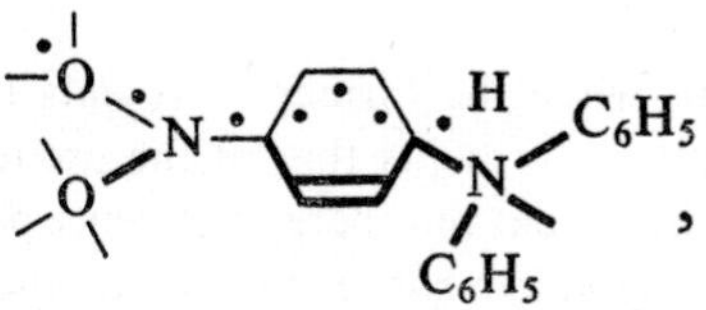

and onto the product

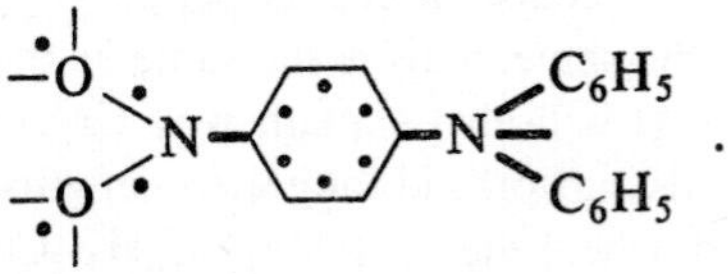

At no stage is there need to assign a formal charge of $-\frac{1}{2}$ to a ring carbon atom; this charge is, in fact, taken up by one of the oxygen atoms of the nitro-group. With benzene, or phenol, or aniline, the formal charge of $-\frac{1}{2}$, which must be absorbed by the rest of the molecule when attack by the negatively charged $N(C_6H_5)_2^-$ occurs, is located on a carbon atom. Consequently the energy of the intermediate is much higher and attack is much more difficult than on nitrobenzene. Other anionoid reagents that will attack aromatic systems are OEt^- and CN^-.

6.5 The Molecular Structure of some Dyes

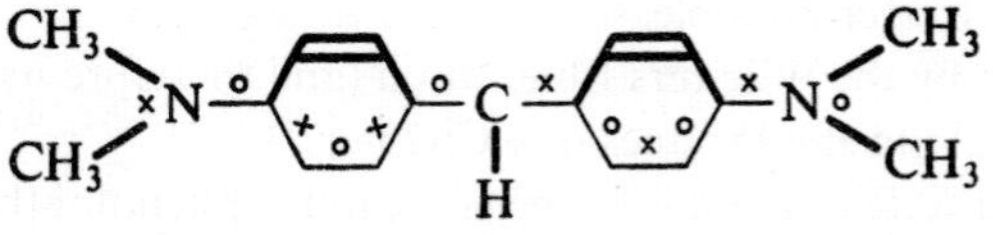

Mischler's Blue absorbs light at long wave-lengths, at the red end of the visible spectrum. It contains the cation $(Me_2N.C_6H_4.CH.C_6H_4NMe_2)^+$. According to the hypothesis being pursued in this book, its structure would be expected to be a hybrid of four structures equivalent to and three equivalent ones. The main merit of this structure is that it divides the single positive charge between the two nitrogen atoms, placing a formal charge of $+\frac{1}{2}$ on each. The above structure also implies a greater separation of the electrons of different spin than does the formula

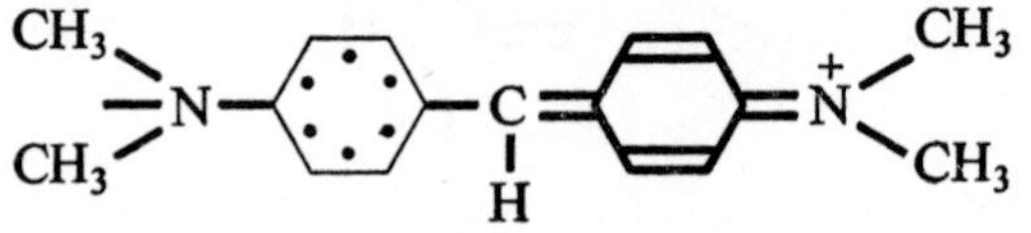

It is possible that, while the former represents the structure of the ground state, the latter represents that of the excited state. Mischler's Blue absorbs red light so that the energy difference per gramme molecule is about 45 kcal. If the above suggestion is true there are eleven more close electron-pairs in the excited state than in the ground state. This would mean that the increase in energy per close pair would be 4 kcal, other things being the same. This is the same as the figure deduced for CO_2 in section 4.5. It will also explain why Crystal Violet containing $[(Me_2NC_6H_4)_3C]^+$ also absorbs at long wave-lengths, and why a solution in fairly strong acid, where the ion $[(Me_2NC_6H_4)_2C(C_6H_4NHMe_2)]^{++}$ is present, also absorbs near 6000 Å. On the other hand, in very strong acid, the ion present is $[(Me_2NC_6H_4)C(C_6H_4NHMe_2)_2]^{+++}$ for which the only possible structure is

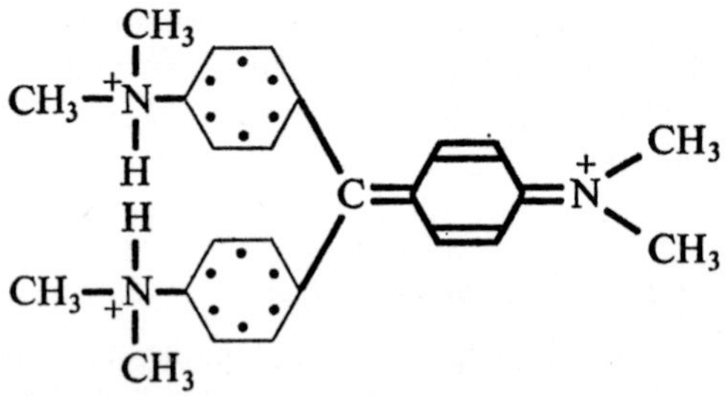

This only absorbs at the blue end of the visible region (4000 Å); the pair of structures between the transition which led to absorption in the red region are no longer possible.

Absorption by the Würsters Blue cation (and therefore its colour) can be explained along similar lines (see Chapter 7).

The ground state of the double negative ion of phenolphthalein, which

is the red form existing in alkaline solution, may have a similar type of structure (with equivalent forms):

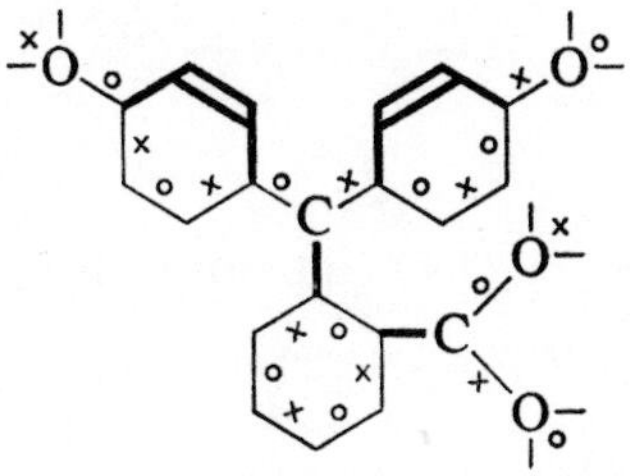

In this case the double negative charge is divided equally between the four oxygen atoms, there being a formal charge of $-\frac{1}{2}$ on each. The structure has some analogy with that of the semiquinonoid ion (see Chapter VII). The structure of the negative ion of fluorescein is likely to be similar to the above.

Many examples of a similar type are provided by the cyanine dyes. These consist of the two systems capable of carrying a positive charge which are separated by a long conjugated chain of CH units. An example of such a structure is

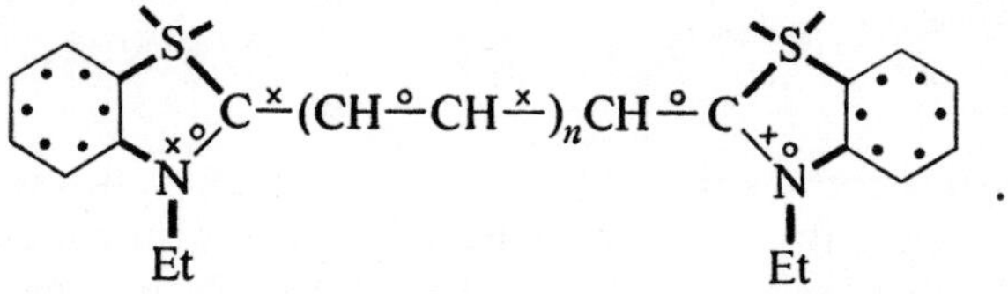

In these ions the charge of +1 is divided equally between the two nitrogen atoms. They absorb light at the red end of the visible, or even in the infra-red, the wave-length increasing as the length of the chain increases.

6.6 Azoxybenzene and Nitrosamines

Azoxybenzene is usually described by the formula

$$\begin{array}{c} C_6H_5\text{—}N\text{=}N\text{—}C_6H_5. \\ \downarrow \\ O \end{array}$$

However, in CF_3NONCF_3, Jander and Haszeldine (*J.C.S.*, 1954) have assigned a frequency of about 1270 cm^{-1} to the NO group. This implies a structure

$$CF_3-N\overset{\times}{-}\overset{\circ}{N}-CF_3$$

containing a three-electron NO bond, rather than

$$CF_3-N{=}N-CF_3$$

In the former the charge distribution in the ONN system is $-\frac{1}{2}, +1, -\frac{1}{2}$ while in the latter it is $-1, +1, 0$. The presence of a charge of $-\frac{1}{2}$ on the second nitrogen is rather unsatisfactory but, in this case, it may be rendered less objectionable because of the adjacent CF_3 group. The first structure has the additional advantage of reducing inter-electron repulsion compared with the second.

The dialkyl nitrosamines also contain the NNO grouping. The NO characteristic frequency of 1430 to 1460 cm^{-1} suggests that the structure is a hybrid of

$$R_2\overset{\times}{N}\overset{\circ}{-}N\overset{\times}{-}O \quad \text{and} \quad R_2N-N{=}O .$$

The formal charge distributions are $+\frac{1}{2}, 0, -\frac{1}{2}$ and 0, 0, 0 respectively. Therefore the latter is favoured by the charge distribution, but the former by the separation of electron pairs. The comparison with CF_3NONCF_3 is interesting because, in that case, the structure containing electron pairs did not have such a favourable charge distribution and, as a result, had less importance. As would be expected nitrosamines do not dimerize (see section 5.5).

6.7 Benzofuroxans and Benzofurazan

Benzofuroxan has the formula $C_6H_4N_2O_2$ and was originally thought to be *ortho*-dinitroso-benzene with the formula

$$C_6H_4(N{=}O)_2 .$$

However, experiments using physical techniques, such as NMR, have shown that the nuclear arrangement is that in the formula

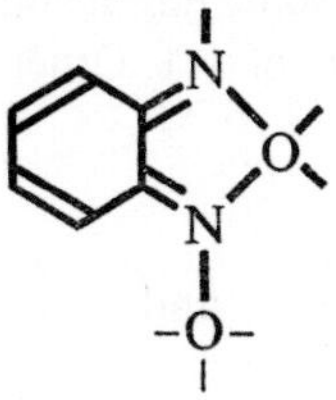

(The electronic structure is that given by A. R. Katritsky, Oksne and Harris, *Chem. and Ind.*, 1961; see also Englert, *Z. Naturf.*, 1961). However, it is very difficult to see why this should be preferred to the dinitroso structure; there is no gain in the number of bonding electrons, the benzenoid ring system is lost and the atoms, which would have zero formal charges in *ortho*-dinitroso-benzene, would have charges of 0, 0, +1, −1 in the NONO system in the latter structure. The situation is clearly analogous to the dimerization of mono-nitroso compounds which was considered in section 5.5.

Possible structures involving bonds containing an odd number of electrons are:

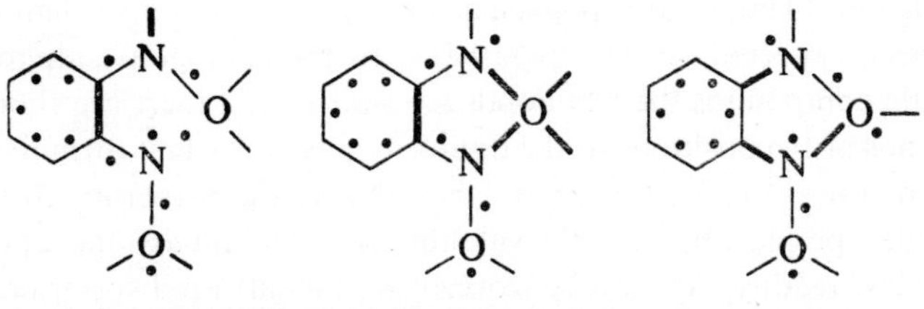

(there are others as well.) The advantages of the above structures would be that inter-electron repulsion would be reduced compared with both the earlier structures. Unfortunately no firm conclusion can be reached because the infra-red spectra of this compound, and its derivatives, are so complicated that they cannot be interpreted with any certainty.

Benzofurazan can be assigned the Lewis-type structures (as far as the NON system is concerned):

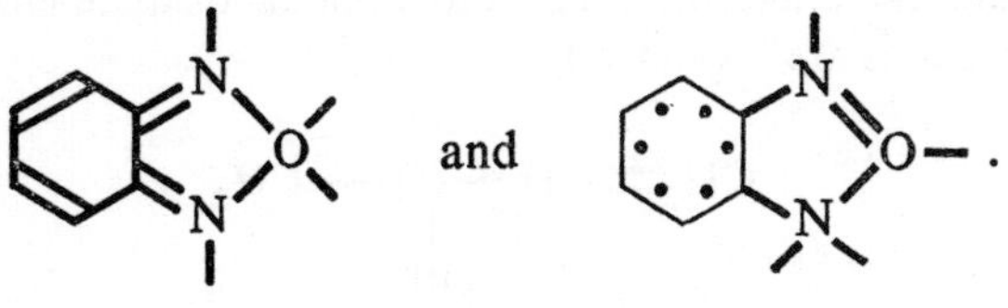

and .

The NO bond length is short (1·20 Å) which virtually excludes the first structure, even though it places a zero formal charge on each atom. The second structure is not likely to be important because one of the nitrogen atoms carries a formal charge of -1. Other possible structures are

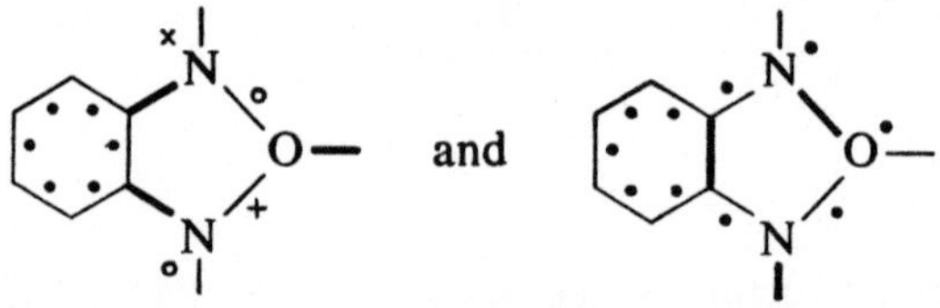

and

together with the mirror image of the latter. The first of these separates electrons but it places a formal charge of $-\frac{1}{2}$ on both the nitrogen atoms; the electrons of both spin-sets favour the same shape. The second places formal charges of $-\frac{1}{2}$, $+\frac{1}{2}$, and 0 in the NON system. It separates electrons, but those of one spin-set favour a different shape at one nitrogen atom than the other. It is probable that all three structures have some importance – though the NO bond length might have been expected to be a little greater (however, the experimental accuracy is not high). The CN bond lengths of 1·35 Å (cf. $C_3N_3H_3$, 1·32, and $(CH_3)_2C{=}NOH$, 1·29) are consistent with the above interpretation. The CC ring bond-lengths are all given at 1·45 Å, which is longer than would have been expected on any hypothesis. In the analogous sulphur and selenium compounds the CN bonds are shorter and there are short ring CC bonds at the positions of the double bonds of the first formula given for benzofurazan. This suggests that this is the structure for these molecules, perhaps because the sulphur and selenium assume a positive charge less readily. As with benzofuroxan, the infra-red spectra cannot be interpreted because of their complexity.

6.8 Addition to Butadiene and Heptatriene

The initial reaction is that of addition of one bromine atom according to (for butadiene):

$$C_4H_6 + Br_2 \longrightarrow C_4H_6Br^+ + Br^-.$$

The bromine can either be attached to a middle or to an end atom; the two positive ions are respectively:

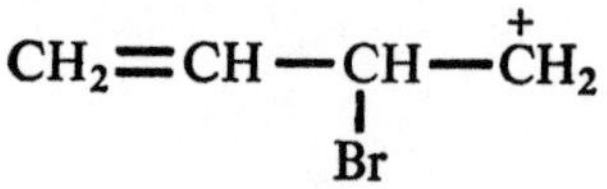

$$CH_2{=}CH{-}\underset{\displaystyle Br}{\underset{|}{CH}}{-}\overset{+}{C}H_2$$

and $CH_2 \overset{\bullet}{-} CH \overset{\bullet}{-} CH — \underset{|\atop Br}{CH_2}$.

The latter is clearly much preferred, because it spreads the formal positive charge over two atoms instead of concentrating it on one, and also it separates the electrons to a great extent, so reducing the inter-electron repulsion energy. Addition to an end carbon atom is therefore favoured. The intermediate positive ion is converted to the dibromide by attack by a negative Br^- ion. The final result can be either $CH_2Br.CH{=}CH.CH_2Br$ involving 1:4 addition, or $CH_2{=}CH.CHBr.CH_2Br$ involving 1:2 addition. Because of the electron affinity of the near-by bromine atom, the carbon atom next to the CH_2Br group can probably accept the addition of negative charge better than the terminal CH_2 group. This would mean that 1:2 addition would be favoured kinetically relative to 1:4 addition. However, in particular cases, solvent and steric effects might also be important. Also, the 1:4 product is thermodynamically more stable than the 1:2 product so that, if any rearrangement of the product occurs, the 1:4 product will be favoured.

With hexatriene the first bromine atom will be attached to the terminal carbon atom in the intermediate ion

$$C \overset{\bullet}{-} H_2CH \overset{\bullet}{-} CH \overset{\bullet}{-} CH \overset{\bullet}{-} CH—CH_2Br^+.$$

The reason why addition at other carbon atoms is not so favoured is the same as for butadiene. The bromide ion can, in principle, attack this ion in the 2, 4 or 6 positions; attack in positions 3 or 5 would result in an odd electron being left on a carbon atom, where it would not be involved in bonding; such a situation would be unsatisfactory energetically. The three transition states for attack by the bromide ion would be

$$CH_2 \overset{\bullet}{-} CH \overset{\bullet}{-} CH \overset{\bullet}{-} CH \overset{\bullet}{-} CH—CH_2Br$$
$$\bullet$$
$$—Br—$$
$$|\bullet$$

$$CH_2{=}CH—CH \overset{\bullet}{-} CH \overset{\bullet}{-} CH—CH_2Br$$
$$\bullet$$
$$—Br—$$
$$|\bullet$$

$$CH_2 \overset{\bullet}{-} CH \overset{\bullet}{-} CH \overset{\bullet}{-} CH \overset{\bullet}{-} CH—CH_2Br$$
$$\bullet$$
$$—Br—$$
$$|\bullet$$

The first and last will have a lower energy than the middle one, because they reduce inter-electron repulsion to a greater extent. Therefore it is possible to understand why 1:4 addition to hexatriene does not take place but only 1:2 and 1:6.

Lithium alkyl, providing a negative alkyl ion, will attack butadiene to give, in the first place, the ion

$$R{-}CH_2{-}\dot{C}H \overset{\cdot}{-} \dot{C}H \overset{\cdot}{-} CH_2.$$

The electronic structure at the end three carbon atoms is that of an allyl negative ion; it is iso-electronic with the system in ozone and is given an analogous structure. This negative ion can attack another butadiene molecule to give, for example,

$$R{-}CH_2{-}CH{=}CH{-}CH_2{-}CH_2{-}\dot{C}H \overset{\cdot}{-} \dot{C}H \overset{\cdot}{-} CH_2.$$

The process can then be repeated so that a polymer of the diene is obtained.

6.9 Claisen Condensation

The application of this hypothesis to the Claisen condensation will be considered. An example of this reaction is the condensation of a ketone, $RCOCH_3$, with ethyl benzoate under the influence of a base, such as sodium ethoxide, to give a β-ketonic ester. The first stage is the removal of a proton from the ketone to give

$$\begin{array}{c} \diagdown\dot{O}\diagup \\ \cdot| \quad \cdot \\ R{-}C \underset{\cdot}{-} CH_2. \end{array}$$

The negative charge is divided between the end atoms in the OCC system; such a structure will therefore be preferred to

$$\begin{array}{c} | \\ {-}O{-} \\ | \\ R{-}C{=}CH_2 \end{array} \quad \text{or} \quad \begin{array}{c} \diagdown O \diagup \\ \| \quad | \\ R{-}C{-}CH_2 \end{array}$$

which concentrate the formal negative charge on one atom. Also the electrons of one spin are separate from those of the other, so reducing inter-electron repulsion. This negative ion will be reactive because of the formal charge of $-\frac{1}{2}$ on the carbon atom, and it will attack the ethyl benzoate, passing through the transition state

$$\mathrm{R{-}\overset{\overset{\dot{O}}{|}}{C}\,{\cdot}\,CH_2 \cdot \underset{\underset{C_6H_5}{|}}{\overset{\overset{O}{\|}}{C}} \cdot \dot{O}Et}$$

to form $RCOCH_2COC_6H_5$ with the release of the negative ion OEt^-. In the transition state the structure

$$\mathrm{R{-}\overset{\overset{\dot{O}}{|}}{C}\,{\cdot}\,CH_2 \cdot \underset{\underset{C_6H_5}{|}}{\overset{\overset{\dot{O}}{|}}{C}}{-}OEt}$$

may also be important. In both structures that have been assigned to the transition state, the negative charge is divided equally between two oxygen atoms so that the energy will not be expected to be high; this explains why the reaction occurs readily in the way it does.

6.10 Oxidation of Secondary Alcohols

Ross Stewart and van der Linden (*Disc. F.S.*, 1960) have suggested that the radical ion

$$\mathrm{(Ar)(CF_3)C{-}O\cdot}$$

may be formed as an intermediate in the permanganate oxidation of the corresponding secondary alcohol. On the double-quartet hypothesis, this would be

$$\mathrm{(Ar)(CF_3)\overset{\times}{C} \overset{\circ}{-} O}.$$

With this formulation, the intermediate would have only half a bond less than both the reactant,

$$\begin{array}{c} \text{Ar} \searrow \overset{\text{H}}{\underset{|}{\overset{|}{\text{C}}}} - \overset{|}{\underset{|}{\text{O}}} -, \\ \text{CF}_3 \nearrow \end{array}$$

and the product ketone. With the first structure these would be one whole bond less. However, the intermediate will be expected to have poor stability because the carbon atom carries a formal charge of $-\frac{1}{2}$; hence it will be easily oxidized by permanganate to the ketone.

6.11 Formulae Used

In some cases, particularly in larger molecules, it is difficult to decide whether a given pair of electrons should be regarded as a *close* pair or not, and therefore whether a heavy or light line should be used in the formula. This occurs when two electrons are shared between two atoms and the disposition of the double-quartet at one atom is such that the electrons of different spin are separated, while that at the other atom is such that the octet is disposed as four close-pairs. In examples of this kind the single bond between the two atoms has been represented in this book by a *heavy* line. An example of a formula in which this problem arises is that for Mischler's Blue (bottom of p. 95); the bonds between the nitrogen and methyl groups are of this kind.

CHAPTER SEVEN

Free Radicals

7.1 Introduction

This chapter will be devoted to molecules and ions containing an odd number of electrons. In Chapter 3, nitric oxide and the superoxide ion were discussed, and it was found that, using the double-quartet form of the octet rule, satisfactory formulae could be written for them which accounted satisfactorily for their properties. In Chapter 4, nitrogen dioxide was also discussed, and in Chapter 5, HO_2 and CH_3O_2. In this chapter a more general consideration will be given to a wide range of free radicals, and it will be found that, for many which show a surprising stability, it is possible to write formulae of the type used for NO, O_2^- and NO_2. However, for others, such as, for example, triphenylmethyl, no such formulae are possible.

7.2 Di-aryl Nitric Oxides

The oxidation of diphenyl hydroxylamine by silver oxide, under very dry conditions, produces a solution which is deep red. From this solution crystalline diphenyl nitric oxide can be obtained. It has the formula $(C_6H_5)_2NO$. Cryoscopic measurements also show that it is monomeric and, even when cooled considerably, it does not form the dimer. Its methoxy- and nitro-derivatives are paramagnetic. Its electronic structure can be described by

$$\begin{matrix} C_6H_5 \searrow \\ C_6H_5 \nearrow \end{matrix} \overset{\times}{N} \overset{\circ}{—} \overset{\times}{\underset{|}{O}} — \quad .$$

Every atom has a double-quartet of electrons, and the formal charges on the nitrogen and oxygen atoms are $+\frac{1}{2}$ and $-\frac{1}{2}$, both of which are acceptable (see Table 3).

The crystals of di-*p*-anisyl nitric oxide have been studied by X-ray diffraction and the NO bond length is 1·23 Å. This is approximately the same length as that in CH_3NO_2 (1·22), in which the NO bonds are also expected to contain three electrons. The characteristic NO frequency observed for diphenyl nitric oxide is 1350 cm^{-1} (Otting and Kainer, *Ber.*, 1954). This is intermediate between the value in CH_3NO (1564 cm^{-1}) and that in $R_3N—O$ (950–970 cm^{-1}). The above structure, therefore, accounts very satisfactorily for the properties of this radical. It also accounts for the stability because, if dimerization occurred, there would be no increase in the number of bonding electrons (cf. NO) and, moreover, the number of close electron pairs would increase so that the rise in inter-electron repulsion energy would operate to stabilize the monomer, relative to the dimer.

Diphenyl nitric oxide reacts with nitric oxide to give diphenyl hydroxylamine and

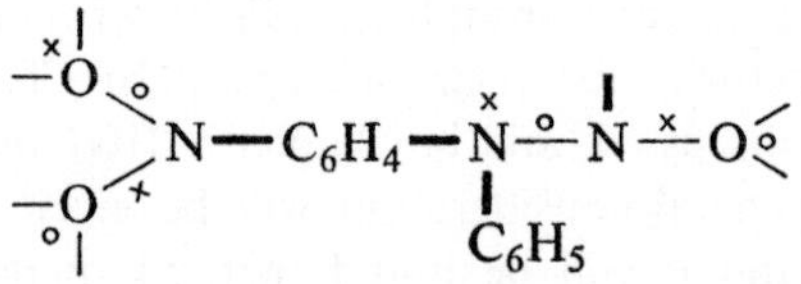

$$\begin{array}{l} -\overset{\times|}{O} \\ \quad\quad\diagdown \\ \quad\quad\quad N—C_6H_4—\overset{\times}{N}\overset{\circ}{—}\overset{|}{N}\overset{\times}{—}O \\ \quad\quad\diagup \\ -\underset{\circ|}{O} \qquad\qquad\qquad\quad |\\ \qquad\qquad\qquad\qquad\quad C_6H_5 \end{array}$$

so that, in one of the products, there is a considerable degree of separation of the electrons of one spin from those of the other. This could explain why the reaction with NO does take place, whereas dimerization does not. Diphenyl nitric oxide also reacts with triphenylmethyl, but in that case there is an increase of one in the number of bonding electrons, so that it is not surprising that reaction takes place.

The reaction of diphenyl hydroxylamine with acetone also gives a stable free radical (Banfield and Kenyon, *J.C.S.*, 1926) which can be given the formula

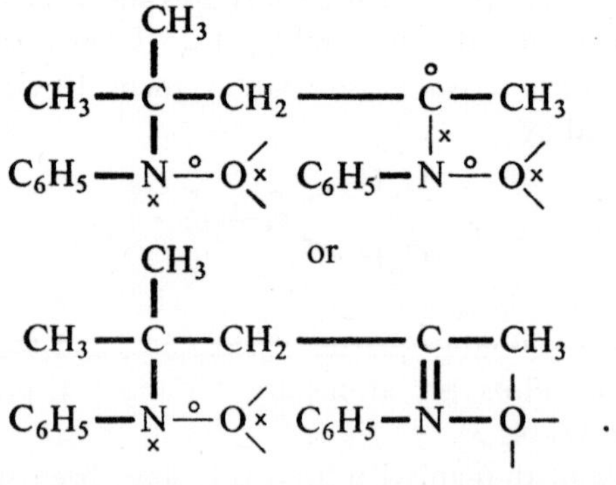

$$\begin{array}{ccccccc} & & CH_3 & & & & \\ & & | & & & & \\ CH_3 & — & C & —CH_2 & —— & \overset{\circ}{C} & —CH_3 \\ & & | & & & |\times & \\ C_6H_5 & — & \underset{\times}{N} & \overset{\circ}{—} O\times & C_6H_5 & — N & \overset{\circ}{—} O\times \end{array}$$

or

$$\begin{array}{ccccccc} & & CH_3 & & & & \\ & & | & & & & \\ CH_3 & — & C & —CH_2 & —— & C & —CH_3 \\ & & | & & & \| & \quad | \\ C_6H_5 & — & \underset{\times}{N} & \overset{\circ}{—} O\times & C_6H_5 & — N & —\underset{|}{O}— \end{array} .$$

Every atom has a double-quartet of electrons in both structures, but, in the first, a carbon atom carries a formal charge of $-\frac{1}{2}$ whereas, in the second, an oxygen atom carries a formal charge of -1. Probably the wave function would be described best by a mixture of the two.

An ion which may have a similar structure is the nitrosodisulphonate ion. Magnetic measurements, using the potassium salt, show that an ion containing an odd number of electrons is present. A possible structure is

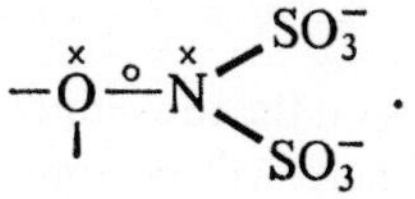

$$-\underset{|}{\overset{\times}{O}}\overset{\circ}{-}\overset{\times}{N}\begin{matrix}\nearrow SO_3^- \\ \searrow SO_3^-\end{matrix} \; .$$

7.3 Hydrazyl Radicals

Triphenyl hydrazine in dry ether is oxidized by lead peroxide at room temperature to give a blue solution containing the radical $(C_6H_5)_2NN(C_6H_5)$. The radical is in equilibrium in solution with the dimer, hexaphenyl tetrazane. On the other hand, the radical $\alpha\alpha$-diphenyl-β-trinitrophenyl hydrazyl is much more stable, and the corresponding tetrazane is unknown. The electronic structure of this radical will be expected to be

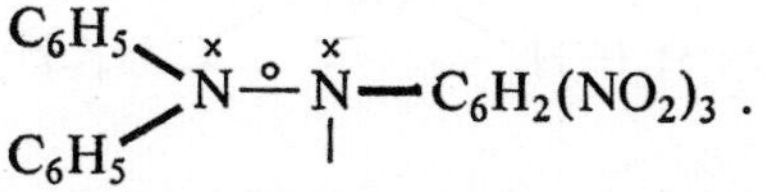

$$\begin{matrix}C_6H_5 \searrow \\ C_6H_5 \nearrow\end{matrix}\overset{\times}{N}\overset{\circ}{-}\underset{|}{\overset{\times}{N}}-C_6H_2(NO_2)_3 \; .$$

The formal charges on the two nitrogen atoms are $+\frac{1}{2}$ and $-\frac{1}{2}$. Now the formal charge of $+\frac{1}{2}$ is acceptable, but that of $-\frac{1}{2}$ is on the limit of what is allowable. The reason why the diphenyl picryl compound is more stable than the triphenyl compound is presumably that the picryl group relieves the adjacent nitrogen atom of some of the negative charge. In the phenyl compound this does not happen so readily and, as a consequence, dimerization to the tetrazane occurs to some degree because, in the dimeric molecule, each of the nitrogen atoms has a formal charge of zero; on the other hand the inter-electron repulsion energy will increase on dimerization.

Comparison may also be made with diphenyl nitric oxide, in which a three-electron bond was also postulated. In that case, the formal charge of $-\frac{1}{2}$ is carried by the oxygen atom. This is more satisfactory than a formal charge of $-\frac{1}{2}$ on a nitrogen atom. It is, therefore, understandable that triphenyl hydrazyl dimerizes to some extent, whereas diphenyl nitric oxide does not.

Triphenyl hydrazyl reacts slowly with nitric oxide to give

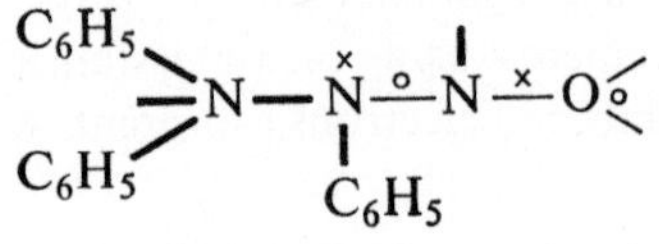

$$(C_6H_5)_2N - \overset{\times}{N}(C_6H_5) \overset{\circ}{-} N \overset{\times}{-} O$$

in which the formal charges on the three nitrogen atoms are 0, $+\frac{1}{2}$ and 0 and on the oxygen $-\frac{1}{2}$. There will be some increase in inter-electron repulsion energy but it must be presumed that the assumption of the nitrogen atoms of more satisfactory formal charges exerts an overriding effect. Triphenylmethyl only reacts slowly with triphenyl hydrazyl; this is probably a result of steric effects.

Another example of a stable ion containing a three-electron bond between two nitrogen atoms is the tetra-*p*-tolyl-hydrazinium cation, to which the following structure can be assigned:

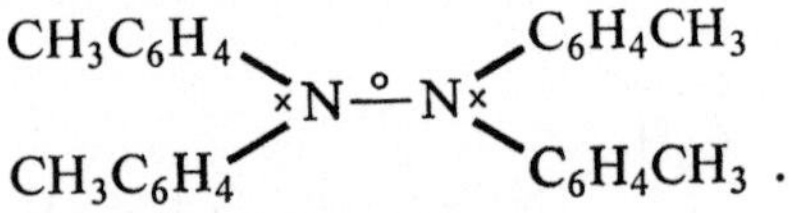

$$(CH_3C_6H_4)_2\overset{\times}{N} \overset{\circ}{-} \overset{\times}{N}(C_6H_4CH_3)_2 .$$

7.4 Semiquinones and Related Substances

When quinone, $C_6H_4O_2$, is reduced in alkaline solutions it is possible to form, as a separate entity, a semiquinone anion $C_6H_4O_2^-$ which is paramagnetic. This involves the addition of one electron to quinone, and is therefore *half-way* to the double negative ion of hydroquinone, $C_6H_4O_2^{=}$, which is diamagnetic. In the case of tetramethyl quinone (duroquinone) the semiquinone exists exclusively as the paramagnetic radical anion. The structure of the semiquinone negative ion may be represented as a mixture of

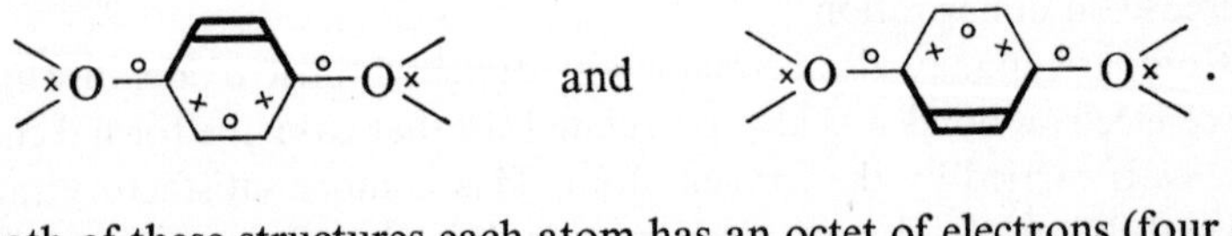

$$\overset{\times}{O} \overset{\circ}{-} C_6H_4 \overset{\circ}{-} \overset{\times}{O} \quad \text{and} \quad \overset{\times}{O} \overset{\circ}{-} C_6H_4 \overset{\circ}{-} \overset{\times}{O} .$$

In both of these structures each atom has an octet of electrons (four of each spin), every carbon atom has a zero formal charge, and each oxygen atom has a formal charge of $-\frac{1}{2}$.

Analogous to the semiquinones are the so-called Würster's salts, which are formed by oxidizing aromatic diamines with bromine. The cation, $R_2NC_6H_4NR_2^+$, they contain will be expected to be a hybrid of

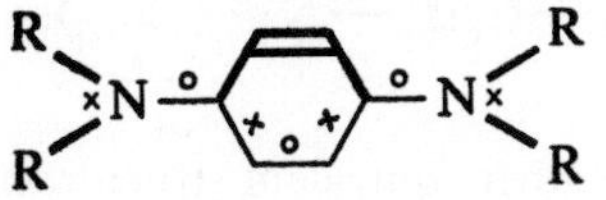

and its mirror image. These salts are strongly coloured (see section 6.5). It has been shown that the NR_2 groups must be *para* to one another and the four attached groups must lie in one plane. In the above formula one spin-set of electrons (circles) favours a planar arrangement, whereas the other (crosses) does not. It seems that the molecule is planar (or transforms from one non-planar form to the inverted one so easily that it is effectively planar).

The blue salt derived by oxidation of tetramethyl-*p*-phenylene diamine is stable, and can be kept indefinitely. On the other hand, no Würster's salt can be obtained from the corresponding compound in which the four hydrogens in the C_6H_4 group are replaced by methyl groups. The explanation for this seems to be that steric hindrance between the methyl groups on the nitrogen atoms and the ring prevent the positive ion being co-planar. Consequently the above electronic structure is not possible, and the radical cation is not formed.

Similar to the Würster's salts are the viologens which can be formed by reducing $\gamma\gamma'$-dipyridyl, or its derivatives, with zinc dust. They are highly coloured, and may be obtained by the oxidation of the derivatives of tetrahydro-$\gamma\gamma'$-dipyridyl. An example of a viologen is

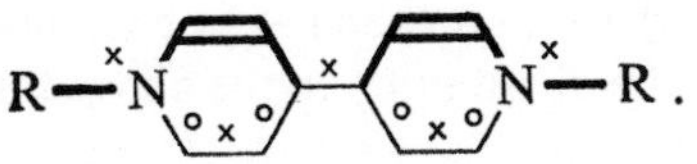

(There are of course three other equivalent structures.) In this radical-ion also each atom has, in its neighbourhood, an octet of electrons and the formal charge on each carbon atom is zero, and on each nitrogen atom $+\frac{1}{2}$. The electron and charge distribution has, therefore, the same satisfactory features as in the Würster's salts.

There are many other examples of relatively stable ions and molecules containing an odd number of electrons which have similarities to the above. For example, Bindschelder's Green, which contains the ion $[(CH_3)_2N.C_6H_4.N.C_6H_4.N(CH_3)_2]^+$, can be reduced to the radical

(again there are three other equivalent structures).

In all these compounds, which are semiquinonoid in type, structures exist which give to each atom a full complement of electrons, and which assign acceptable formal charges to the various atoms. Particularly in the cases where charges of $+\frac{1}{2}$ are assigned to nitrogen atoms, it is not surprising that the radicals are stable.

7.5 Riboflavin

Kuhn and Ströbele (*Ber.*, 1937) used magnetic measurements to show that riboflavin is reduced to leuco-riboflavin in two stages. The intermediate radical stage, in which just one hydrogen atom has been added, can be assigned structures of the type:

The hydrogen atom could be attached to the other end of the semi-quinonoid system, but this would produce formal charges which are much less satisfactory ($-\frac{1}{2}$ on N and $+\frac{1}{2}$ on O, instead of $+\frac{1}{2}$ on N and $-\frac{1}{2}$ on O, which is the distribution in the above formula).

7.6 Paramagnetic Molecular Compounds

Bijl, Kainer and Rose-Innes (*J.C.P.*, 1959) investigated the magnetic properties of various molecular compounds analogous to that formed between $C_6Cl_4O_2$ (chloranil) and $(CH_3)_2NC_6H_4N(CH_3)_2$ (tetramethyl-*p*-phenylene diamine); the two members are such that the transfer of one electron from one of the molecules to the other (e.g. from diamine to chloranil) will produce two semiquinonoid-type radicals. This transfer will occur with no change in the number of species, and with no change in the total number of bonding electrons. It was found that, in some cases, the molecular compounds were paramagnetic, but with other molecules they were not. The formation of the semiquinonoid ions will be favoured by the reduction in inter-electron repulsion energy which results from the separation of electrons of one spin from those of the other in the semiquinonoid species. Opposing the electron transfer will be the electrostatic energy resulting from the separation of the positive and negative charges. The latter effect will depend on the ease with which the diamine loses an electron and the readiness with which the quinone accepts it. The experiments showed that the development of paramagnetism in the compound did, in fact, depend on these properties. The existence of the two opposing factors explains why the transfer takes place in some cases, but in others it does not.

Eley and Inokuchi showed that some of these molecular compounds are semiconductors. In these cases the transfer of the electron from one molecule to another must take place easily.

7.7 Free Radicals Containing Other Elements

Gordy, Ard and Shields (*P.N.A.S.*, 1955) studied the electron spin resonance spectrum produced in proteins and polypeptides containing sulphur when they were exposed to radiation. It was found that, with all these substances, a particular spectrum was obtained on all occasions; moreover, this spectrum was never observed when sulphur was not present. They suggested that the odd electron was localized in the sulphur–sulphur bond and suggested that the structure was

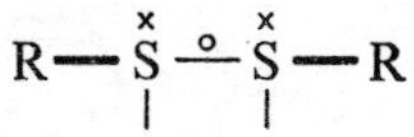

$$R-\underset{|}{\overset{\times}{S}}\overset{\circ}{-}\underset{|}{\overset{\times}{S}}-R$$

(though they depicted it a little differently). Each sulphur has an octet of electrons and a formal charge of $+\frac{1}{2}$.

An example which seems to involve a halogen atom is provided by 9-chloro-10-hydroxy-phenanthrene. This can be oxidized to a peroxide which dissociates partially in solution. The solution is blue and probably contains the radical

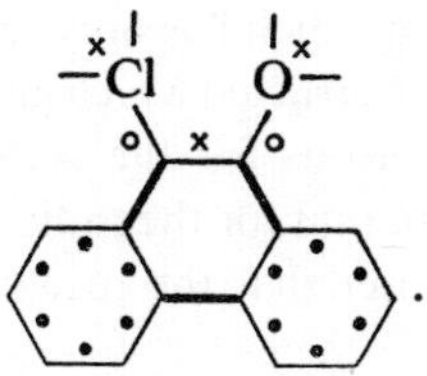

$-\overset{\times}{Cl}$ $\quad \overset{\times}{O}-$

In this there is a formal charge of $-\frac{1}{2}$ on the oxygen atom and $+\frac{1}{2}$ on the chlorine atom. This may be the reason why it only dissociates partially, even though the dissociation leads to a radical in which there is some separation of electrons of one spin from those of the other.

7.8 Triphenylmethyl

It has been known for a long time that hexaphenylethane dissociated appreciably in solution to form two triphenylmethyl radicals. These radicals can be given the formula

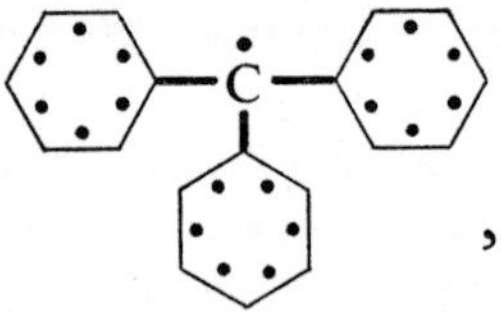

and six of the type

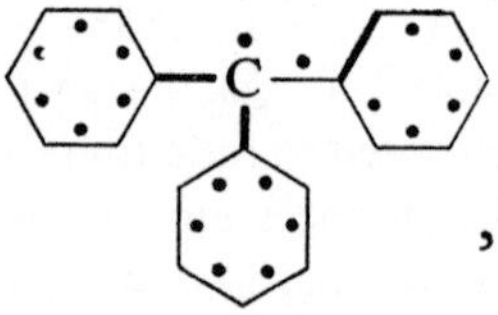

and six of the type

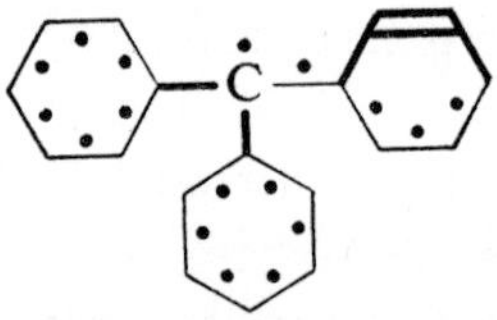

In all thirteen formulae one carbon atom has only seven electrons in its valence shell. The first formula has a zero formal charge on each atom; the other twelve place a formal charge of $-\frac{1}{2}$ on the central carbon atom and one of $+\frac{1}{2}$ on the atom which has only seven electrons in its valence shell. No formula can be constructed which gives to every carbon atom an octet of electrons. The reasons for the stability of this radical must, therefore, be different from that for the radicals discussed in sections 7.2 to 7.7; it will be shown later that the reactivity is, in certain respects, greater.

There are two main reasons for the existence of triphenylmethyl. The first is that steric repulsion effects in hexaphenylethane are considerable, and are reduced on dissociation. The second is that the total wave function is represented by a mixture of wave functions of a relatively large number of different valence-bond forms. This means that, in the electron distribution (wave function squared), the importance of cross-terms (e.g. $\Psi_{I}\Psi_{II}$), of which there are 156, become increasingly important relative to the squared terms (e.g. Ψ_{I}^{2}), of which there are thirteen. The squared terms correspond to the localization of a charge, or of a lone electron, as indicated by the formulae. The cross-terms do not correspond to such a strong localization of either charge or odd electron. The cross-terms correspond therefore to a wider distribution of these unsatisfactory features of the individual structures (which we inevitably visualize in terms of Ψ_{I}^{2}, etc.). The number of cross-terms is $n(n-1)$, where n is the number of structures, whereas the number of squared terms is n. Thus, as n increases, the importance of the cross-terms increases. Therefore the presence of the three phenyl groups attached to the central carbon atom allows the odd electron to be located in a wide variety of places and, by the above effect, spreads out any localization of charge or of free valency.

However, it still remains true that, when two radicals join together, an additional bond is formed. Also when triphenylmethyl combines with nitric oxide to give $(C_6H_5)_3CNO$ there is an increase of one in the number of electrons in bonds. For this reason it is not surprising that nitric oxide reacts instantaneously with triphenylmethyl. A similar reaction occurs with NO_2 to give $(C_6H_5)_3CNO_2$ and $(C_6H_5)_3ONO$; the explanation is the same. Likewise, oxygen reacts with triphenylmethyl to give the peroxide $(C_6H_5)_3C—O—O—C(C_6H_5)_3$, in this case there is an increase of one in the number of bonding electrons per radical.

On this basis it is therefore possible to understand why triphenylmethyl and related species are more reactive than most of the radicals that have been considered earlier in this chapter. On the other hand, it is possible to understand why they exist.

Tetraphenyl hydrazine, $(C_6H_5)_2NN(C_6H_5)_2$, is a stable colourless substance at room temperature. However, if its solutions in non-ionizing solvents are heated, they become green. The colour disappears on cooling. Undoubtedly dissociation occurs to $(C_6H_5)_2N$. The existence of this can be discussed in the same terms as that of triphenylmethyl which it resembles; it reacts rapidly with nitric oxide to give diphenylnitrosamine.

It is interesting that the behaviour of $(C_6H_5)_2N$ can be contrasted with $(C_6H_5)_2N.NC_6H_5$; the latter has a much smaller tendency to associate than the former. For the latter, it has been shown that a structure in which each atom has an octet of electrons is possible (section 7.3). On the other hand, for $(C_6H_5)_2N$, no structure is possible in which each atom has an octet. The distinction between the two types of radical is demonstrated clearly by this pair of examples.

7.9 Oxidation of Benzoin

There are a number of reactions which pass through intermediates which are radicals. In the case of the oxidation of benzoin the intermediate radical is sufficiently stable to be observed.

In aqueous-methanolic solution containing alkali, benzoin, $C_6H_5CO.CHOH.C_6H_5$, is oxidized by air to benzil, $C_6H_5.CO.CO.C_6H_5$. The latter contains two electrons less than the double negative ion of the former. The intermediate contains one electron less than the reactant and one more than the product. The three species are 7.I, 7.II, and 7.III. When a solution of 7.I is shaken in air, the appearance of colour shows the formation of 7.II. When this solution is again shaken the colour disappears as 7.III is formed from 7.II. However, it quickly returns as

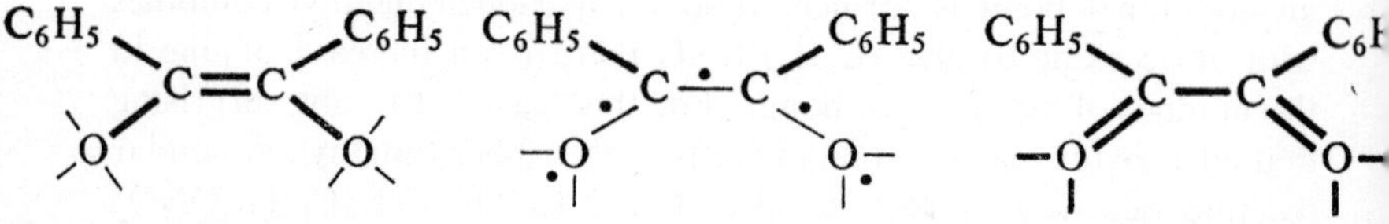

7.I   7.II   7.III

7.III reacts with more 7.I to give more 7. II. This provides an example of two species containing $2n$ and $2n+2$ electrons respectively, reacting together to give two molecules of the intermediate species containing $2n+1$ electrons. This takes place because, in the intermediate 7.II, inter-electron repulsion is reduced, the electrons of one spin being separated from those of the other. In both 7.I and 7.III there are several electron-pairs occupying the same spatial orbital.

7.10 Autoxidation of Aldehydes

In the autoxidation of benzaldehyde, perbenzoic acid is formed. Radical intermediates are probably involved in this reaction but they cannot be isolated. It is probable that the first step in the reaction is the production of the radical RCO. This will have the formula

$$C_6H_5-\overset{\times}{C}\overset{\circ}{=}\overset{\times}{O}-\,.$$

However, the formal negative charge on the carbon will make this very reactive. If oxygen is present it will form

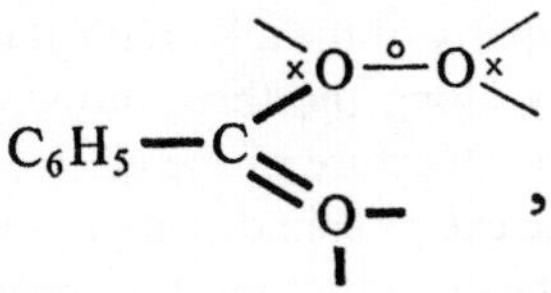

$$C_6H_5-C\begin{matrix} \diagup\,{}^{\times}O\overset{\circ}{-}O^{\times} \\ \diagdown\!\!\diagdown\, \underset{|}{O}- \end{matrix}\quad ,$$

in which the formal negative charge of $-\frac{1}{2}$ has been transferred to an oxygen atom. This benzoyl-peroxy radical will therefore be expected to be more stable than the benzoyl radical from which it is formed. The benzoyl-peroxy radical can then abstract a hydrogen atom from another molecule of benzaldehyde forming perbenzoic acid and a new benzoyl radical, so that a chain reaction is set up.

The above mechanism involves two intermediate radicals for which formulae satisfying the octet rule exist. The pattern of formal charges suggests that the benzoyl-peroxy radical will be the more stable. Moreover, in this radical, the electrons of one spin favour the same shape as the electrons of the other spin; this is not the case for the benzoyl radical. Consequently, in an oxidizing mixture of benzaldehyde, the stationary concentration of the benzoyl-peroxy radical may not be very small. If this is so, it would explain why a mixture of benzaldehyde and air is much more reactive than perbenzoic acid. It will oxidize anthracene, which perbenzoic acid itself will not; and it can even oxidize carbon tetrachloride giving hydrogen chloride, phosgene and other substances.

Other similar examples could be quoted but space does not permit an extension of the application of this hypothesis to any further radical reactions of this kind.

7.11 The Allyl Radical

This is an unstable free radical but it is formed by the irradiation of allyl compounds and can be detected in the material by electron spin resonance. D. M. Hirst (Oxford) has made an extensive theoretical study of this radical and concludes that its structure is represented more satisfactorily by a mixture of wave functions corresponding to $\dot{C}H_2 \overset{\bullet}{-} CH \overset{\bullet}{-} CH_2$ and $CH_2 \overset{\bullet}{-} CH \overset{\bullet}{-} \dot{C}H_2$, than by a mixture of wave functions corresponding to $CH_2{=}CH{—}\dot{C}H_2$ and $\dot{C}H_2{—}CH{=}CH_2$. The former is also more satisfactory than a simple molecular orbital formulation. The performance of the different functions was judged by the energy calculated using them; the lowest calculated energy being the best (Hirst and Linnett, *J.C.S.*, 1962, 1963).

The only physical property of the allyl radical that is known is the disposition of spin density along the three atom systems; this has been determined from the fine structure of the electron spin resonance spectrum. It is found that the excess spin density is over-concentrated on the end atoms so that, on the central atom, the density of the spin which is not in excess exceeds that which is in overall excess; there is said to be negative spin density on the central atom. The Lewis–Pauling valence-bond formulae predict too high a negative spin density on the central atom; the molecular orbital too low a negative spin density (zero, in fact). The formulae not involving electron pairs predict an intermediate value, which is, however, rather larger than the experimental figure. The calculations were carried out for the three electrons of the π-system only and it may be that the neglect of the electrons of the σ-system is serious. Further work is being done on the calculation of spin densities in systems of the kind using a variety of functions, some of which are modifications of molecular orbital functions, while others are modifications of the more localized descriptions.

7.12 Conclusion

In this chapter the structures of a number of stable and fairly stable free radicals have been discussed. It has been found that most of the stable free radicals can be assigned formulae which satisfy the double-quartet modification of the octet rule for all atoms. It is, therefore, possible to understand the stability of these radicals; for instance, why they do not dimerize to give molecules containing an even number of electrons, and why they are not attacked by substances such as nitric oxide. As in the earlier chapters it is found that the use of formal charges is helpful in assessing the stability of the various structures.

The structure of triphenylmethyl and related radicals has also been examined. The structural situation is different in these cases; it has been discussed briefly.

The success of the double-quartet method in accounting for the stability of free radicals such as diphenyl-picryl-hydrazyl is a direct consequence of the use of a localized description and the continued employment of the octet rule. It was pointed out in section 3.8 that, for diatomic molecules and ions, the present formulation is very close to a molecular orbital formulation. However, it would not be easy to extend the M.O. treatment to *all* of the wide variety of species that have been treated in Chapters 5, 6 and 7, with comparable results, particularly as for several of the molecules a simultaneous consideration of the σ- and π-systems is necessary; that is, the whole electronic structure had to be considered.

CHAPTER EIGHT

Further Inorganic Examples

8.1 Introduction

Several of the molecules considered in Chapters 3, 4 and 5, were of inorganic substances, but almost all of those in the last two chapters were of organic substances. The object of this chapter is to illustrate, with a few selected examples, ways in which these ideas can be helpful in formulating structures for a wider range of inorganic substances than have been discussed so far. The selection that has been made includes hydrogen bonds and hydrogen bridges, oxides and oxyanions, silicon and phosphorus compounds, carbonyls and nitrosyls.

The structural proposals of some sections of this chapter must be more tentative than those made earlier in this book. This cannot be avoided because the expansion of the valence shell beyond the octet does inevitably increase the range of structures that are possible. So few calculations have as yet been carried out for molecules containing silicon, phosphorus, sulphur or chlorine atoms that it is not possible to speak with as much conviction of structures containing these elements as of those involving only elements having atomic numbers less than that of neon.

8.2 Hydrogen Bonds and Hydrogen Bridges

The simplest hydrogen bond is that in the FHF^- ion, which is present in crystals of potassium hydrogen fluoride. The FF distance in this ion is 2·26 Å and the proton lies midway between the two fluorine atoms. The HF distance is therefore 1·13 which is 0·21 greater than the distance in molecular HF. The heat evolved when FHF^- (gas) is formed from gaseous HF and F^- has been calculated by Waddington to be about 60 kcal/g ion (*Adv. I. and R-C.*, 1959).

The electronic structure of this ion can be described by

$$\overset{\times}{—}\underset{|}{\overset{|}{F}} \circ H \times \underset{|}{\overset{|}{F}}\overset{\circ}{—} .$$

If Lewis-type structures only are used then it would be described as a resonance hydrid of F—H F^- and F^- H—F. Either representation can account for the proton having a minimum of energy when it is in the centre. However, the first formula implies a greater separation of the electrons from one another than does the resonance description, so that it is likely to correspond to a lower energy, and therefore be a better representation.

The boron hydrides have structures in which protons lie between two boron atoms and it seems that their electronic structures bear some relation to that of FHF^-, though there are great differences because the molecules of the boron hydrides are electron deficient. The best known boron hydride is B_2H_6 (diborane), but an even simpler one, namely $B_2H_7^-$ probably exists. It is thought that this ion is formed when diborane is passed into a solution of lithium borohydride (Brown *et al.*, *J.A.C.S.*, 1957). The stoichiometry indicates that

$$2BH_4^- + B_2H_6 \longrightarrow 2B_2H_7^-$$

occurs. The nuclear magnetic resonance spectrum of the solution is consistent with this interpretation. The structure of the ion is likely to be $H_3B.H.BH_3$, the electronic structure being

$$\begin{array}{lcccr} \mathrm{H} & & & & \mathrm{H} \\ \mathrm{H}\!-\!\mathrm{B} & \times & \mathrm{H} & \circ & \mathrm{B}\!-\!\mathrm{H}\,. \\ \mathrm{H} & & & & \mathrm{H} \end{array}$$

B. J. Duke (Oxford) has made calculations for the central system, and his results show that the above provides a better description of the structure than a three-centre bond formula, in which both electrons occupy an orbital spreading over the *three* central atoms. This might be represented by

$$\begin{array}{lcr} \mathrm{H} & & \mathrm{H} \\ \mathrm{H}\!-\!\mathrm{B} & \overline{\quad\mathrm{H}\quad} & \mathrm{B}\!-\!\mathrm{H}\,. \\ \mathrm{H} & & \mathrm{H} \end{array}$$

It is also better than the resonance description using the two valence-bond structures

$$\begin{array}{lr} \mathrm{H} & \mathrm{H} \\ \mathrm{H}\!-\!\mathrm{B}\!-\!\mathrm{H} & \mathrm{B}\!-\!\mathrm{H} \\ \mathrm{H} & \mathrm{H} \end{array} \quad \text{and} \quad \begin{array}{lr} \mathrm{H} & \mathrm{H} \\ \mathrm{H}\!-\!\mathrm{B} & \mathrm{H}\!-\!\mathrm{B}\!-\!\mathrm{H}\,. \\ \mathrm{H} & \mathrm{H} \end{array}$$

It is not difficult to see that the structure involving the two one-electron bonds implies a reduction in the inter-electron repulsion energy relative to the other two. By allowing the two electrons independent 'movement' in a three-centre system, the three-centre bond allows the electrons a fairly considerable chance of being near one another. The resonance description using valence-bond structures, by putting the electrons as pairs into bonds, enhances the repulsion even more. The first structure, by keeping the electrons in separate bonds, implies a reduction in inter-electron repulsion energy, but it still maintains two bonding electrons.

On the same basis, the structure of B_2H_6 would be expected to be described most satisfactorily by

```
H      H      H
 \   •   •   /
  B   :   :  B  .
 /   •   •   \
H      H      H
```

An alternative description is to use two three-centre bonds

```
H      H      H
 \   /‾‾‾\   /
  B         B
 /   \___/   \
H      H      H
```

(this is equivalent to Pitzer's protonated double bond formulation). Also, valence-bond structures may be employed:

```
H     H     H                 H     H     H
 \   /     /                   \     \   /
  B      B       and            B      B    ,
 /     /   \                   /   \     \
H     H     H                 H     H     H
```

together with smaller contributions from

```
H     H     H                 H     H     H
 \   /     /                   \     \   /
  B      B       and            B      B    .
 /   \     \                   /     /   \
H     H     H                 H     H     H
```

The structure using two three-centre bonds implies the widest range of disposition of the four electrons. The only correlation implied is that two electrons tend to be on one side of the $BH_2 \ldots BH_2$ plane, and two on the other. The valence-bond structures imply some further correlation, namely that both electrons of a pair tend to be in one BH bond or the other; the greater weight of the first pair of structures above implies that the two electron pairs will have a greater probability of being on opposite sides of the $B\overset{H}{\underset{H}{\;}}B$ diamond than on adjacent sides. The latter effect is reasonable, but the association in pairs is unreasonable. The first structure involving one-electron bonds, implies that the distribution of the pair in each three-centre bond is modified so that one electron is towards one end of the region while the other electron is towards the other. This is a very reasonable effect because it keeps all four electrons in bond regions (i.e. under the influence of two nuclei), but reduces inter-electron repulsion by keeping the four electrons apart. As would be expected, calculations using a wave function based on the first structure lead to a lower energy than those using wave functions based on the other structures (three-centre bonds, or valence bond with resonance). Duke's calculations also show that the four electrons in the four BH one-electron bonds tend to be attracted more to the protons than to the boron atoms. This means that, on the whole, the hydrogens tend to carry a negative charge, though, of course, the *formal* charge on each of the atoms is zero.

Duke's calculations have not been extended beyond $B_2H_7^-$ and B_2H_6 but it does seem that similar ideas can be used with other hydrides. For instance B_4H_{10} would be given the structure

```
                  H
                  |
 H      . H • B • H .      H
   \              |           /
    B :           |         : B
   /              |           \
 H      • H . B . H •      H .
                  |
                  H
```

The external BH bond lengths are 1·19 Å (cf. 1·187 in B_2H_6). The B—H bonds have lengths of 1·34 and 1·43 (cf. 1·334 in B_2H_6). The bonded BB distance is the shortest in the molecule (1·73 Å). The structure gives a zero formal charge to each atom. In broad outline, therefore, the above electronic structure accounts for the nuclear arrangement.

8.3 Expansion of the Valence Shell

So far the molecules and ions considered have contained only elements of the First Short Period, and we have been mostly concerned with compounds of carbon, nitrogen, oxygen and fluorine. For these elements the valence shell is that of quantum number 2 and, because the subsidiary quantum number can only be zero or 1, the capacity of the valence shell is eight electrons. The basis of the earlier chapters has been that this octet of electrons is made up of two spin-sets of four. In the next period (sodium to chlorine), the electrons of the valence shell are in orbitals of quantum number 3. Those orbitals of subsidiary quantum number (l) 0 and 1 are more tightly bound than those having $l = 2$ (see Fig. 6). Consequently, in some compounds such as PH_3, H_2S, HCl, $(CH_3)_2S$ and many others, only the 3*s* and 3*p* orbitals are used and the electronic structures are similar to those of the corresponding compounds of nitrogen, oxygen and fluorine. However, in other compounds, such as PF_5, SF_6, ClF_3, H_2SO_4, and others, it seems probable that the shell

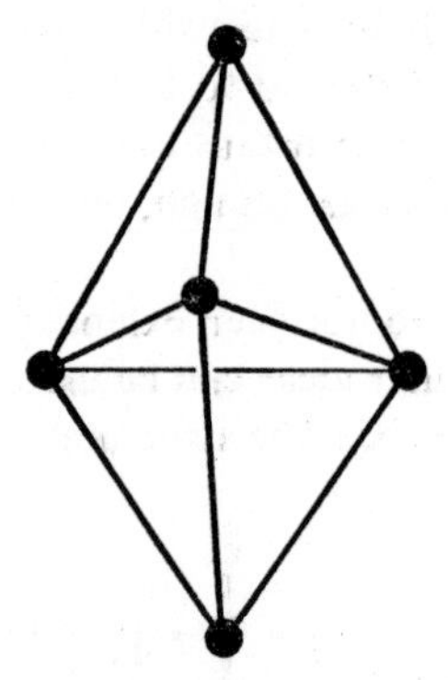

FIG. 18. Trigonal bi-pyramidal arrangement.

of electrons round the central atom (P, S or Cl above) contains more than eight electrons. This is possible because the 3*d* orbitals can be used as well as the 3*s* and 3*p*. Since elements in the First Short Period cannot have more than eight electrons in the valence shell, there are no compounds analogous to PF_5, etc., for elements in the First Short Period.

With the octet, both the two spin-sets of four had a tetrahedral arrangement. With five electrons of the same spin, the most probable arrangement is with them disposed at the corners of a so-called trigonal bipyramid (see Fig. 18), this can be visualized as: one at the north pole, one at the south pole and three on the equator of the corners of an equilateral triangle. With six electrons of the same spin, the most probable arrangement is with them located at the corners of a regular octahedron with the nucleus at the origin. Alternatively they may be visualized at the middle of each face of a cube; or on the Cartesian axes,

$+r$ and $-r$ on the x-axis, $+r$ and $-r$ on the y-axis, and $+r$ and $-r$ on the z-axis. These three methods of regarding this arrangement are shown in Fig. 19; sometimes one is more helpful than another. However, it

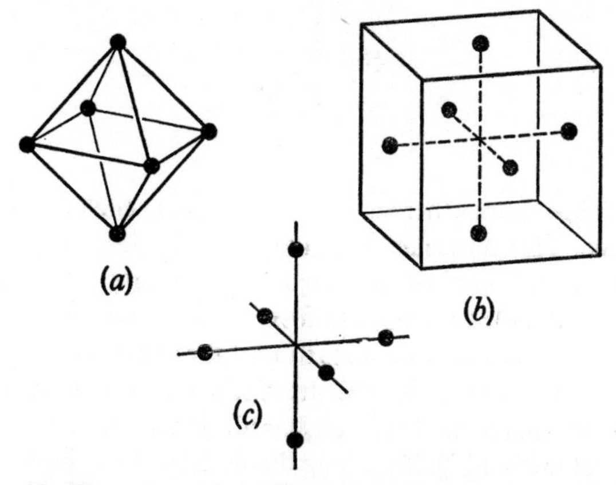

FIG. 19. Three ways of visualizing the octahedral disposition of particles; (*a*) At the corners of an octahedron; (*b*) at the centres of the six faces of a cube; (*c*) at equal distances from the origin along the three Cartesian axes.

must be remembered that it is always described as an *octahedral* arrangement.

In sulphur hexafluoride, electron-pair bonds are formed to each fluorine, the shell of twelve electrons being provided as follows: six from the sulphur and one from each of the fluorines. Round the sulphur atom there are two spin-sets of six electrons, each being octahedral. In order to bind the six fluorine atoms the two spin-sets have the same orientation providing six pairs. The structure may be represented by

```
          |
         -F-
   ≥F–    |    –F≤
       ╲  |  ╱
          S
       ╱  |  ╲
   ≂F–    |    –F≂.
         -F-
          |
```

Each fluorine has a double-quartet of electrons while the sulphur has a double-sextet; all atoms have zero formal charges.

In phosphorus pentafluoride the phosphorus uses its five electrons, together with five provided by the fluorine atoms, to bind the five atoms in a structure which can be represented by

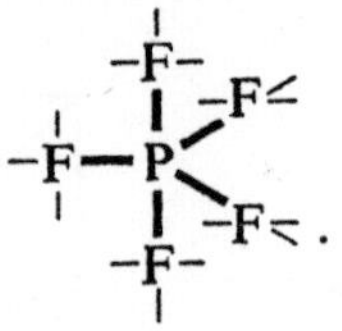

```
       |
      -F-
       |  -F<
 |     | /
-F-----P
 |     | \
       |  -F< .
      -F-
       |
```

Around the phosphorus there is a double-quintet; each atom has a zero formal charge. This molecule can take up an F^- ion to form PF_6^-, the structure of which is analogous to that of SF_6 above.

On the other hand, sulphur also forms a tetrafluoride. The electron-pair bonds to the four fluorines uses four of the sulphur electrons leaving two unused. Therefore, in its valence shell, the sulphur atom has ten electrons, eight shared and two unshared. These ten electrons form a double-quintet (as in PF_5), arranging themselves as five pairs as is necessary to bind the fluorines most effectively; there are four shared-pairs and one lone-pair, the structure being

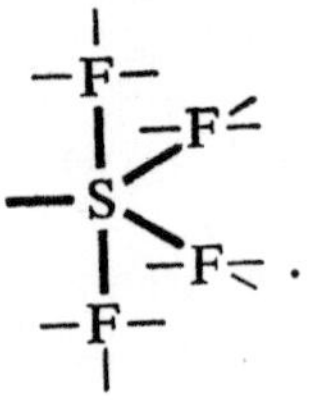

```
       |
      -F-
       |  -F<
       | /
   ----S
       | \
       |  -F< .
      -F-
       |
```

The shape of the molecule is consistent with this.

Similarly, iodine forms iodine pentafluoride in which the iodine has a shell of twelve electrons, seven provided by the iodine atom and five provided by the fluorine atoms. Of these, there are five shared-pairs and one lone-pair. The structure is

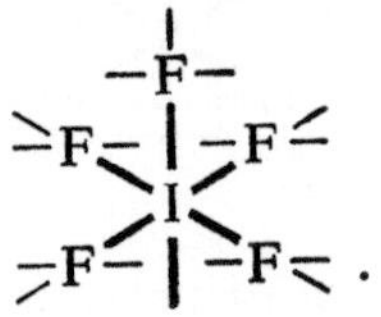

```
         |
        -F-
   >F-   |   -F<
      \  |  /
         I
      /  |  \
   >F-   |   -F< .
```

The iodine atom has in its valence shell a double-sextet.

In chlorine trifluoride there are ten electrons in the valence shell of the chlorine atom; there are three shared-pairs and two lone-pairs. The structure is

```
      |
     -F-
      |      |
   >Cl---F-,
      |      |
     -F-
      |
```

the chlorine atoms have a double-quintet of electrons arranged as five pairs.

The approach used in the earlier chapters for the octet can therefore be extended to larger groups of electrons, which may be described as double-quintets or double-sextets (as in PF_5 and SF_6). In some complexes (e.g. $Mo(CN)_8^{4-}$), a double-octet of electrons (i.e. 16) is present. The octet (eight electrons of the same spin) can be arranged in two ways as shown diagrammatically in Fig. 20. These are as a square antiprism, or at the corners of a dodecahedron (see Fig. 20). In the TaF_8^{3-} ion, in

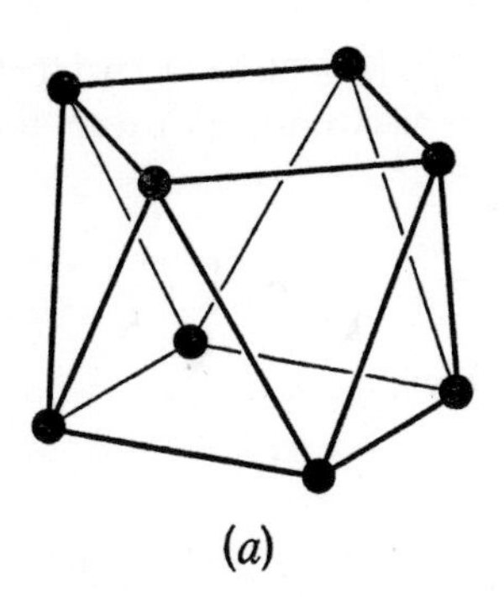

(*a*)

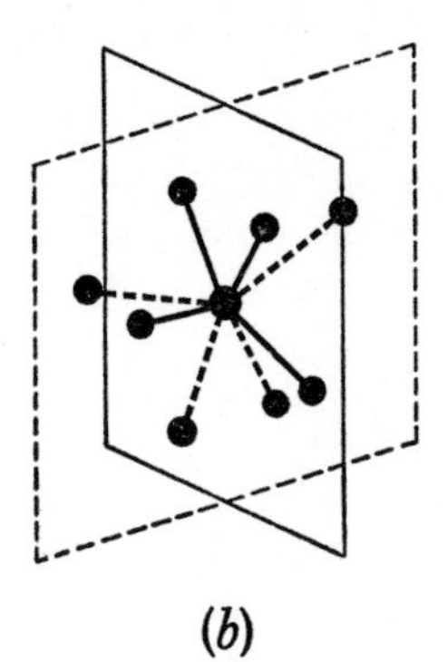

(*b*)

FIG. 20. Two arrangements of eight particles round a centre; (*a*) square-antiprism; (*b*) dodecahedral apices.

Na_3TaF_8, the fluorine atoms are at the corners of a square antiprism; in the $Mo(CN)_8^{4-}$ ion in $K_4Mo(CN)_8.2H_2O$ the carbon atoms are at the apices of a dodecahedron.

The common arrangement of the five electrons in a quintet is at the corners of a trigonal bipyramid (cf. PF_5). However, calculations suggest that the arrangement of five at the corners of a square-based pyramid (cf. Fig. 21), has a probability only a little smaller than that of the trigonal bipyramid. There do not seem to be any molecules which have this shape, but it is possible that this arrangement of five electrons does

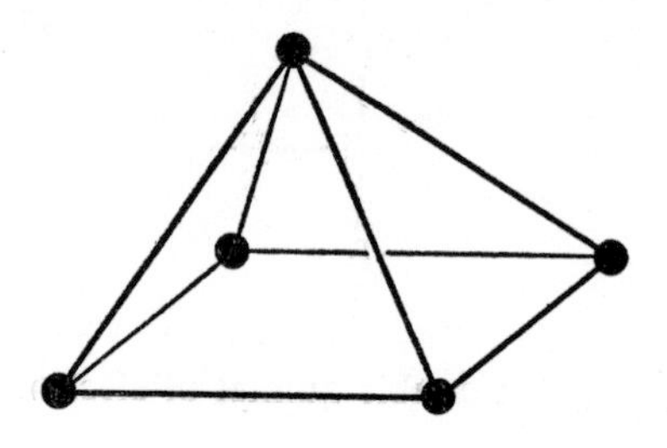

FIG. 21. Square-based pyramidal arrangement.

exist in the $(PNCl_2)_n$ ring compounds. This will be examined later (section 8.6).

In the next few sections a number of compounds of the elements from silicon to chlorine will be discussed.

8.4 Some Phosphorus–Oxygen Compounds

The structure of phosphoryl fluoride, POF_3, which places a zero formal charge on each atom and possesses no close electron-pairs, except those in the PF bonds, is

$$\begin{array}{ccccc} & & | & & \\ & & -\mathrm{F}- & & \\ | & & | & & \\ -\mathrm{F} & — & \mathrm{P} \overset{\times}{\underset{\times}{-}} \mathrm{O} \overset{\circ}{\underset{\circ}{-}} . & & \\ | & & | & & \\ & & -\mathrm{F}- & & \\ & & | & & \end{array}$$

The PO bond length of 1·48 Å is not inconsistent with this structure when comparison is made with other PO bond lengths. This structure assigns to the phosphorus valence shell a quartet–sextet structure. This will serve to separate the electron of one spin from those of the other in the region of the oxygen atom, with a consequent reduction in inter-electron repulsion. The quartet will favour all interbond angles close to the tetrahedral; the sextet will favour FPF being 90° and FPO being 135°. The FPF angle would therefore be expected to be intermediate between 90° and 110°; it is $102\frac{1}{2} \pm 2°$. Moreover, the ClPCl angle in $OPCl_3$ is given as $103\frac{1}{2} \pm 1°$. In $OPBr_3$ the value given is $108 \pm 3°$ but in this case repulsion between the halogen atoms is likely to be important.

The structure round the phosphorus atom will be expected to be similar to the above in P_4O_{10} and the external PO bond length (1·485) is found to be the same as in POF_3. The P—O—P bond lengths in P_4O_6 and P_4O_{10} are 1·65 and 1·61 respectively. These are presumably single bonds or, at any rate, close to being single bonds.

Phosphoric acid can be titrated, using methyl orange as an indicator, as far as the loss of one proton. But the ion $H_2PO_4^-$ is a weak acid. This means that $H_2PO_4^-$ has neither a high tendency to gain a proton nor to lose one. Its structure will be expected to be

In this structure all atoms have zero formal charges except the two oxygens attached only to phosphorus, which have formal charges of $-\frac{1}{2}$ each. It is, therefore, understandable that this ion has a fairly low proton affinity. Moreover, when a further proton is lost, the resulting $HPO_4^=$ will only have structures which either place formal changes in excess of $-\frac{1}{2}$ on at least one oxygen, or place a negative formal charge on the phosphorus atom. This explains why $HPO_4^=$ has a high proton affinity. The PO bond lengths in $H_2PO_4^-$ are 1·504 and 1·583; these are presumably to be associated with $P\overset{\bullet}{-}O$ and P—O bonds respectively. Both are 0·02 or 0·03 Å shorter than would have been expected, relative to the other PO bond lengths quoted earlier in this section. This shortening in the bond lengths in the ion may be a consequence of the cohesive electrostatic forces between the positive and negative ions in the crystal (cf. the comparisons for SO and ClO bond lengths in the next section).

8.5 Some Oxides and Oxyanions of Sulphur and Chlorine

According to the hypothesis being proposed, the most probable structure of the sulphate ion is

This separates the electrons in the two spin-sets and gives to each oxygen a formal charge of $-\frac{1}{2}$, and to the sulphur atom a zero formal charge and a double-sextet of electrons. This accounts, therefore, for the low proton affinity of the sulphate ion, and for its considerable stability. It is possible that structures which transfer the $-\frac{1}{2}$ from one of the oxygen atoms to the sulphur, involving an SO four-electron bond, have some lesser importance. The SO bond length in the sulphate ion is about 1·44 Å.

The octet structure of sulphur dioxide would be

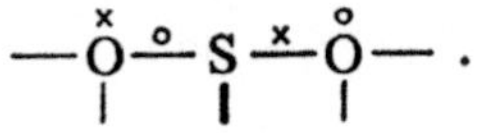

—O—S—O— .

This is analogous to that of ozone, there being a formal charge of +1 on the central atom. With ozone this cannot be modified, and it is unstable. With sulphur dioxide, the sulphur can accommodate more electrons than eight in its valence shell, so that structures

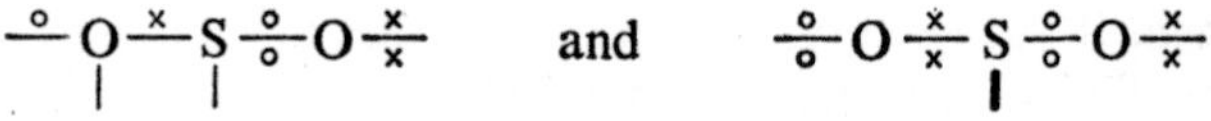

—O—S—O—   and   —O—S—O—

are important, and the molecule is quite stable. The formal charges on sulphur in the two above structure are $+\frac{1}{2}$ and 0 respectively. The SO bond length is 1·43 Å which is less than in the sulphate ion. A decrease is to be expected but it would have been expected to be greater. It is possible that the SO bond lengths in the sulphate ion are reduced by the forces arising from the attraction between opposite charges in the lattice (cf. last section for PO bonds).

A structure similar to the one above for $SO_4^{=}$ could be assigned to the ClO_4^- ion. However, it would place a formal charge of +1 on the chlorine atom. Relative to this, there is likely to be a greater transfer of electrons to the chlorine atom. Structures which give a zero formal charge to the chlorine are then those equivalent to

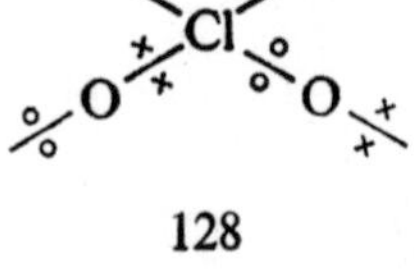

O O
 Cl
O O

in which the chlorine has a double-septet of electrons. The ClO bond length is 1·50 Å. The probable electronic structure of the ClO_2^- ion is

$$\begin{array}{c} \;\;\;\;\;\;\;\;\; |\,{}^{\circ} \\ \;\;\;\;\;\overset{+}{\diagup}\,O- \\ \diagdown Cl \\ \diagup \;\;\;{}^{\circ}\diagdown O- \\ \;\;\;\;\;\;\;\;\; |\,{}^{\times} \end{array}$$

as this gives a zero formal charge to the chlorine atom, and separates the electrons of those two spin-sets. The ClO bond is longer (1·64 Å), as would be expected.

The structure for ClO_2 which places a zero formal charge on each atom is

$$\overset{\times}{\underset{\times}{-}}O\overset{\circ}{\underset{\circ}{-}}\underset{|}{\overset{\times}{Cl}}\overset{\times}{\underset{\times}{-}}O\overset{\circ}{\underset{\circ}{-}}\,.$$

The bond length is 1·49 Å. It is understandable that the length is closer to that in ClO_4^- than to that in ClO_2^-. The reason that it is not even shorter, relative to ClO_4^-, may be again a consequence of a reduction in the ClO bond length in ClO_4^- because of electrostatic forces in the crystal.

8.6 Silyl Compounds

Ebsworth, Jenkins, Mays and Sugden (*Proc. C.S.*, 1963) have shown that the heavy atoms of silyl isocyanate (and isothiocyanate) lie on a straight line, while those of silyl azide are non-linear, like those of methyl azide and isocyanate.

The systems are all H_3AXYZ where A is carbon or silicon, and XYZ is NNN or NCO (or NCS). If A is silicon, the linear structures 8.I to 8.VI are possible, because A can have more than eight electrons in its valence shell.

$H_3A{=}X{=}Y{=}Z{=}$ 8.I

$H_3A{-}X{\equiv}Y{-}Z{\equiv}$ 8.II

$H_3A{\equiv}X{-}Y{\equiv}Z{-}$ 8.III

$H_3A\overset{\times}{-}X\overset{\circ}{=}Y\overset{\times}{-}Z\overset{\circ}{=}$ 8.IV

$H_3A\overset{\times}{=}X\overset{\circ}{-}Y\overset{\times}{=}Z\overset{\circ}{-}$ 8.V

$H_3A\overset{\times}{\underset{\times}{-}}X\overset{\circ}{\underset{\circ}{-}}Y\overset{\times}{\underset{\times}{-}}Z\overset{\circ}{\underset{\circ}{-}}$ 8.VI

$H_3A\overset{\times}{-}\underset{|}{X}\overset{\circ}{-}Y\overset{\times}{=}Z\overset{\circ}{-}$ 8.VII

$H_3A{-}\underset{|}{X}{=}Y{=}Z{=}$ 8.VIII

$H_3A{-}\underset{|}{\overset{\times}{X}}\overset{\circ}{-}Y\overset{\times}{=}Z\overset{\circ}{-}$ 8.IX

Because formal charges of -1, $-1\frac{1}{2}$ or -2 are unsatisfactory on nitrogen (Table 3), structures 8.I, 8.II, 8.IV and 8.VI are impossible for silyl azide. Structure 8.III is also impossible because there is a formal charge of -2 on the silicon atom, and also a triple bond between it and the adjacent nitrogen atom. In 8.V, there is a formal charge of $-1\frac{1}{2}$ on the silicon atom and a five electron bond between it and the adjacent nitrogen atom. Such a structure is unlikely to have a low energy. Consequently there is no satisfactory structure for linear H_3SiNNN. On the other hand, with H_3SiNCO, 8.I, 8.IV and 8.VI place formal charges of 0, $-\frac{1}{2}$ and 0 on Z (now oxygen); they place formal charges of -1, $-\frac{1}{2}$ and -1 on the silicon atom respectively. Structure 8.IV will therefore be expected to be satisfactory, and probably 8.I and 8.VI will have some importance also. Consequently H_3SiNCO will be expected to be linear. For H_3SiNNN, the electronic structure is probably 8.VII; this places formal charges of $-\frac{1}{2}$, 0, $+1$ and $-\frac{1}{2}$ on the four heavy atoms, SiNNN. It is not as satisfactory as 8.IV for H_3SiNCO because there are two fewer bonding electrons. These considerations therefore make it possible for us to understand why H_3SiNCO is linear whereas H_3SiNNN is bent; that is, why the atom at one end of the molecule decides the shape at the other (Linnett, *Nat.*, 1963).

With methyl azide and isocyanate, atom A is restricted to a valence shell of eight electrons. Of those structures considered so far, only 8.II is possible; but this is impossible for both CH_3NNN and CH_3NCO because of the large formal negative charge on atom Z in both cases. Structures 8.VIII and 8.IX have to be considered. Both are satisfactory for CH_3NCO; but only 8.IX is for CH_3NNN. However, both correspond to a non-linear arrangement of the heavy atoms; therefore both methyl compounds are bent.

A rather similar example is provided by trisilylamine and trimethylamine; the heavy atoms in the former are co-planar, while in the latter they are pyramidal. The structure of trisilylamine must be represented by three equivalent structures of the type

H_3Si (×) N (o) SiH_3, with SiH_3 below N.

This will have a formal charge of $+1$ on the central nitrogen atom and $-\frac{1}{2}$ on two of the silicon atoms. Because the valence shell of carbon is restricted to an octet a lone-pair must remain on the nitrogen atom in trimethylamine and the molecule is pyramidal.

Disilyl oxide is non-linear but the SiOSi angle is very large; probably about 160°. Structures that must be considered are:

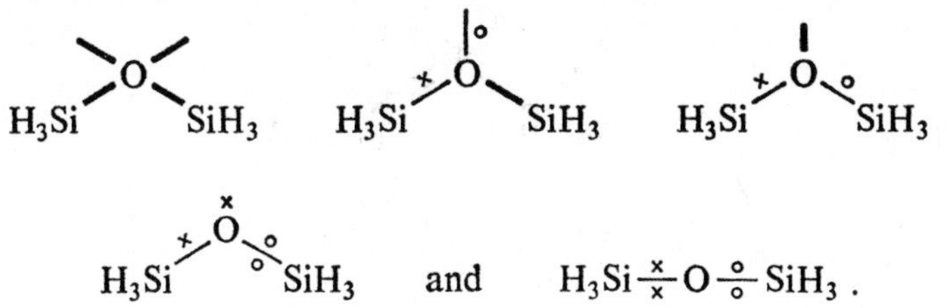

$$H_3Si{-}O{-}SiH_3 \qquad H_3Si\overset{+}{\diagup}\overset{|\circ}{O}{\diagdown}SiH_3 \qquad H_3Si\overset{+}{\diagup}\overset{|}{O}\overset{\circ}{\diagdown}SiH_3$$

$$H_3Si\overset{+}{\diagup}\overset{\times}{O}\overset{\circ}{\underset{\circ}{\diagdown}}SiH_3 \quad \text{and} \quad H_3Si\overset{\times}{\underset{\times}{-}}O\overset{\circ}{\underset{\circ}{-}}SiH_3\,.$$

The formal charges for these five structures are 0, 0, 0; $-\frac{1}{2}$, $+\frac{1}{2}$, 0; $-\frac{1}{2}$, $+1$, $-\frac{1}{2}$; $-\frac{1}{2}$, $+1\frac{1}{2}$, -1; -1, $+2$, -1. From the material used to derive the figures in Table 3, it would have been thought that only the first three structures deserved consideration. But all of these would require an SiOSi angle in the range 100–120°. However, there is another feature that must be taken into account here which had no importance for the molecules and ions considered in the preparation of Table 3. That is, in this molecule, some of the atoms present are able to expand their valence shell beyond the octet so that the five structures above contain 4, 5, 6, 7 and 8 bonding electrons respectively (ignoring the SiH bonds). In this case, therefore, it appears that the increase in the number of bonding electrons to seven makes the fourth structure important even though there is a formal charge of $+1\frac{1}{2}$ on the oxygen atom. In this structure, the electrons of one spin tend to favour a linear arrangement of the heavy atoms while those of the other spin favour a non-linear arrangement. The last structure probably has some importance, but probably less because of the very high formal charge on the oxygen atom (+2). It seems likely that the fourth structure (and its equivalent mirror image) is the most important and that probably the fifth and perhaps also the third have some importance. This method can therefore go some way to helping us understand this very surprising inter-bond angle in $H_3Si{-}O{-}SiH_3$.

The SiOSi angle in a number of silicates is also abnormally large.

8.7 Phosphonitrilic Halides

The compounds that will be discussed here are $(PNX_2)_3$ and $(PNX_2)_4$; most attention will be given to the first. If X = Cl, this is called trimeric phosphonitrilic chloride, or hexachlorotriphosphazene. The molecule contains a six-membered ring and it was first described in terms of a Kekulé-type resonance hybrid, one of the structures being

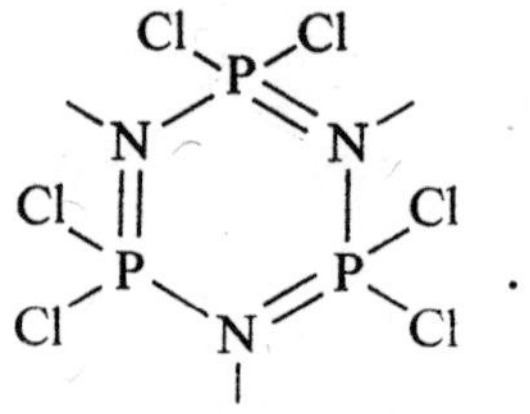

Later, Craig and Paddock (*Nat.*, 1958), and Dewar, Lucken and Whitehead (*J.C.S.*, 1960) formulated orbitals for this molecule; neither set of orbitals appears to be wholly satisfactory.

At each phosphorus and nitrogen atom let z be the direction perpendicular to the plane of the ring and x an axis directed to the centre of the ring, y is then a 'tangential' axis. The important nitrogen orbitals will be s, p_x, p_y and p_z; the important phosphorus orbitals will be s, p_x, p_y, p_z and d_{xz}.

On a molecular orbital basis the s, p_x and p_y orbitals of the nitrogen atoms will be used to construct the σ orbitals, while p_z will contribute to the π orbitals of the ring. The ring σ orbitals of the phosphorus will be hybrids of the s, p_x and p_y orbitals; the orbitals involved in the PCl bonds will be hybrids of s, p_x, p_z and d_{xz}; a hybrid of the p_z and d_{xz} orbitals will contribute to the π molecular orbitals of the ring. Using these orbitals the π molecular orbitals can be constructed in an analogous manner to those of benzene, or, more correctly, to those of $C_3N_3H_3$. There is no need to lay particular stress on three-centre bonds as was done by Dewar *et al.* The fact that the PCl bonds involve orbitals which are hybrids involving d orbitals makes it understandable that the ClPCl angle is less than the tetrahedral, despite the size of the chlorine atoms; the ClPCl angle in $P_3N_3Cl_6$ is 102°.

In the section dealing with benzene (6.2) the relation between the molecular orbital and the valence-bond structures was described, together with the relation of the M.O. formulation to a three-electron bond description. It was found that calculations using the three-electron bond formula gave the lowest energy. This suggests that $P_3N_3Cl_6$ would be described better by than by any other simple formula. Such a structure can be described as aromatic, in the sense that it will be expected to have a lower energy than that of one of the Kekulé forms, because of the reduction in inter-electron repulsion energy (this is only part of the meaning of the word *aromatic* as it is used in reference to benzene).

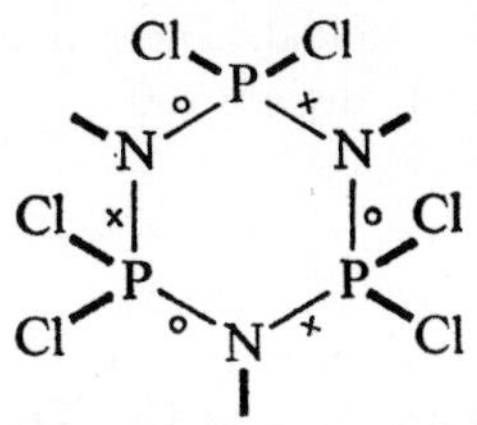

The disposition of electrons round the nitrogen atom is satisfactory as both spin-quartets favour the same shape but are disposed differently. At the phosphorus atom there are two quintets. Each quintet may be visualized as being disposed approximately as a square-based pyramid; the electron at the apex is towards one nitrogen atom, the bisector of the directions to two of the others is towards the other nitrogen atom, and the remaining two electrons of each quintet bind the chlorine atoms. The electron disposition might also be visualized in terms of a trigonal bipyramid, but the symmetry makes this less satisfactory; calculation has shown that the trigonal bipyramidal disposition of the electrons is only slightly more probable than the square-based pyramidal (Linnett and Mellish, *T.F.S.*, 1953). The arrangement of electrons round the phosphorus atom is, therefore, as satisfactory as that round the nitrogen atom; and it explains the magnitude of the ClPCl angle.

The compound $P_4N_4Cl_8$ will be expected to have the structure:

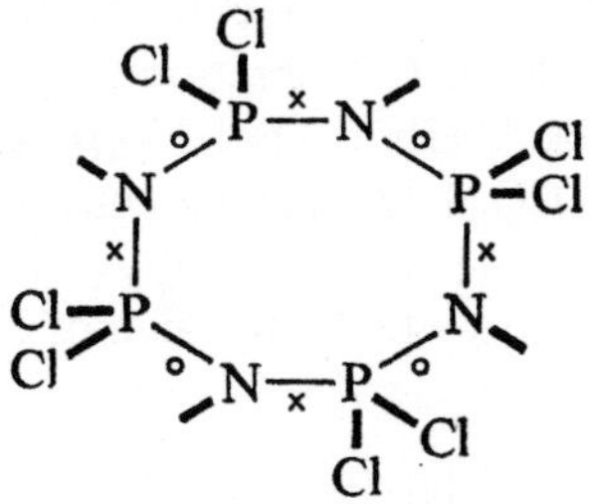

The ClPCl angle is $105\frac{1}{2}°$ and the NP bond length is the same as in the trimeric compound. The ring is puckered which may mean that the electron arrangement at each phosphorus atom is, in this molecule, more closely trigonal-bipyramidal. There is a corresponding fluorine compound in which the FPF angle is 100°.

8.8 Metal Carbonyls

The transition metals form a large variety of carbonyls of the formula $M(CO)_n$ (e.g. $Ni(CO)_4$, $Fe(CO)_5$ and $Cr(CO)_6$) and a number of iso-electronic ions (e.g. $Fe(CO)_4^{2-}$, $Mn(CO)_5^{-}$ and $Mn(CO)_6^{+}$. If it is presumed that the carbon monoxide molecule shares two of its electrons with the metal atom, then the latter has a number of electrons, shared and unshared, equal to the number in the krypton atom.

Taking $Ni(CO)_4$ as an example, if the NiC bonds are just electron pairs (i.e. coordinate links from the carbon to the nickel), the formal charge on the nickel will be -4 and on each oxygen atom $+1$. However, another possibility is that the nickel and carbon atoms might be joined by three electron bonds, the formula of the molecule being

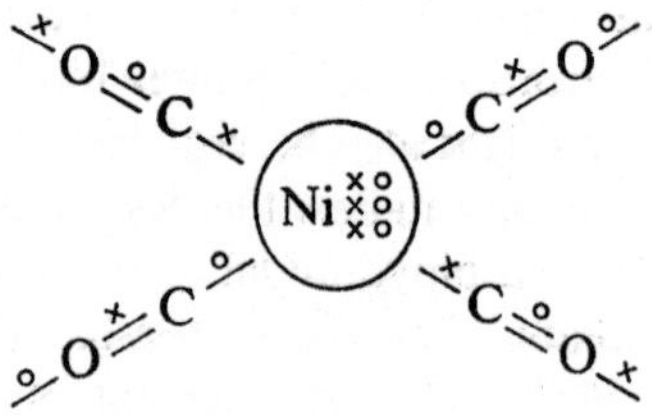

In this structure each oxygen would have a formal charge of $+\frac{1}{2}$ and the nickel atom one of -2. If the structure is this, then the CO bond is a five-electron one and would be expected to be weaker than the bond in carbon monoxide (six-electron). In fact the CO characteristic frequency of $Ni(CO)_4$ is 2057, while the CO vibration frequency is 2170 cm^{-1}. The CO bond length in nickel carbonyl is $1{\cdot}15 \pm 0{\cdot}02$. This is a little longer than the triple bond in CO (1·13 Å) and is consistent with a five-electron bond.

It would be possible to write the formula of $Ni(CO)_4$ with bonds of the type

$$Ni \overset{\times}{\underset{\times}{-}} C \overset{\circ}{\underset{\circ}{-}} O \overset{\times}{\underset{\times}{-}}$$

which would even out the formal charges to a still greater extent. However, from the characteristic vibration frequency and the bond length, it does not seem that the order of the CO bond is reduced so much. It appears that the structure shown above provides a satisfactory explanation of nickel carbonyl. The formal charge of -2 on the nickel atom is presumably acceptable because the carbon atoms, having a greater electronegativity than the nickel atom, polarize the electron cloud and hence make the real charge distribution more even.

A similar structure is possible for $Fe(CO)_4^{2-}$, which is found in $K_2Fe(CO)_4^{2-}$. However, this would give a formal charge of -4 to the iron atom. This would be reduced to -2, if the structure

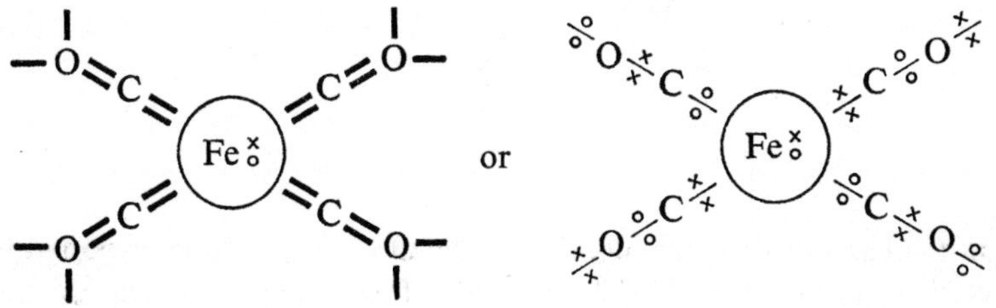

were adopted. If this were the structure the CO bond order would be reduced. The observed characteristic frequency of 1786 cm^{-1} shows that this has occurred. Since the CO frequency in H_2CO is 1760, and in Cl_2CO 1810 cm^{-1}, it is not unreasonable to suppose that the above formulae, involving CO bonds of order two, provide a reasonable approximation to the actual structure. It appears that the assumption that the formal charge on the metal atom is -2 is not unreasonable, as judged by those results. The corresponding ion $Co(CO)_4^-$ would then be expected to be described by a mixture of wave function corresponding to a set of structures equivalent to

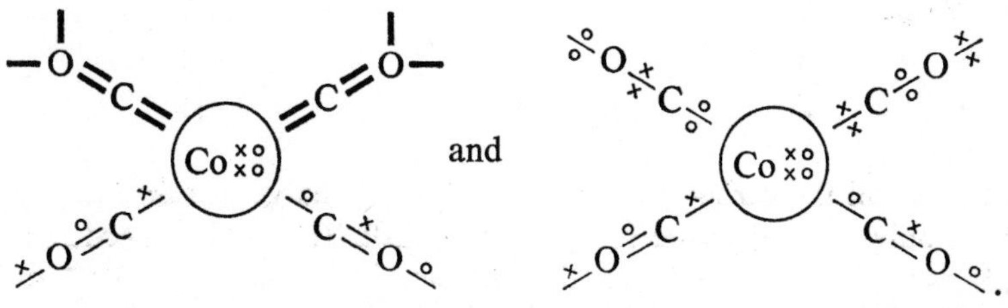

Again the formal charge on the metal atom is -2. The CO bond order is $2\frac{1}{4}$ and the characteristic frequency is 1886 cm^{-1}.

For the $Mn(CO)_6^+$, the structure which gives to the metal atom a formal charge of -2 is

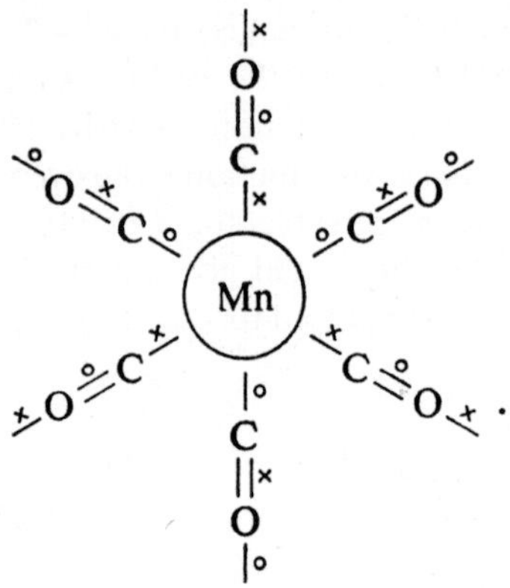

On the basis of this formula, the CO bond order would be expected to be $2\frac{1}{2}$, as in $Ni(CO)_4$. The characteristic frequency is 2090 cm^{-1}, compared with 2057 cm^{-1} in $Ni(CO)_4$. For $Cr(CO)_6$ and $V(CO)_6^-$ the following structures (or sets of ones equivalent to them) will give to the metal atom a formal charge of -2:

and

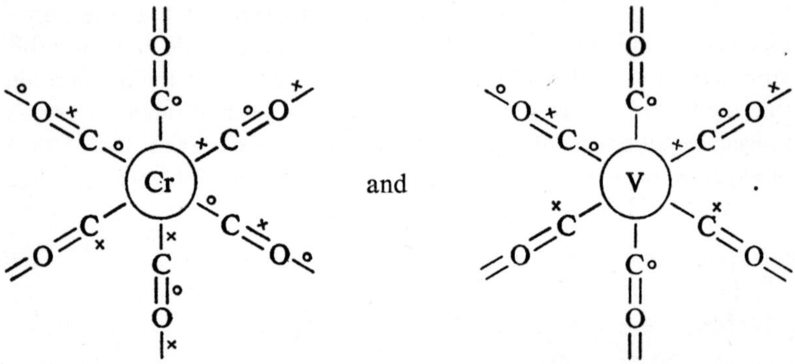

In these all the carbon atoms have a formal charge of zero but some have only seven electrons in the valence shell. The CO bond orders are $2\frac{1}{3}$ and $2\frac{1}{6}$ respectively and the characteristic frequencies 1981 and 1859 cm^{-1}.

For $Fe(CO)_5$ and $Mn(CO)_5^-$, structures which give a formal charge of -2 to the metal atoms are and

The CO bond orders are 2·4 and 2·2 and the characteristic frequencies are 2024 cm^{-1} and 1880 cm^{-1}.

The CO bond orders and characteristic frequencies are shown graphically in Fig. 22. It will be seen that there is, for these eight molecules

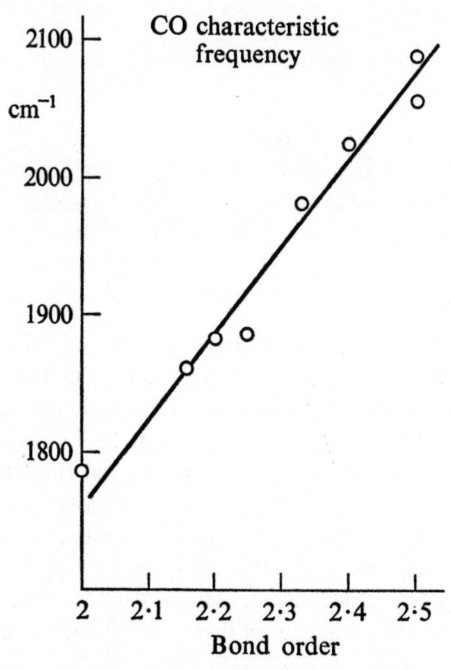

FIG. 22. Graph of CO characteristic frequency against CO bond order (see text) for various metal carbonyl molecules and ions.

and ions, an extremely good correlation between the characteristic frequency and the bond order. Abel (*Q.R.C.S.*, 1963) has given a table which sets out the variation of characteristic frequency for each type ($M(CO)_4$, $M(CO)_5$, $M(CO)_6$). Using the assumption that the formal charge on M in these species will be close to -2, it has been possible to bring the three sets together. The reason this has been possible may be that, in these eight species, the same ligand is linked to the metal in all cases.

In $PF_3Ni(CO)_3$, the mean CO frequency is 2078 cm^{-1}. This implies that the phosphorus atom will form a bond to the nickel with an order greater than one and, since the frequency is about the same as that in $Ni(CO)_4$ (2057), that the tendency to form a multiple bond is about the same for the PF_3 ligand as for CO. The formula is then

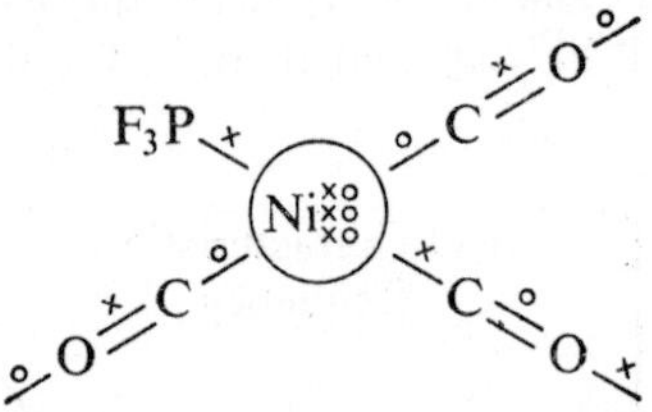

In $PMe_3Ni(CO)_3$ the CO frequency is 40 or 50 cm^{-1} less than in $PF_3Ni(CO)_3$ implying that the PF_3 forms a multiple bond by accepting electrons from the nickel atoms more readily than PMe_3. This is to be expected because of the high electronegativity of fluorine.

8.9 Metal Nitrosyls

Iso-electronic with nickel carbonyl are the nitrosyl compounds $Co(NO)(CO)_3$, $Fe(NO)_2(CO)_2$ and $Mn(NO)_3CO$. The metal-carbon bond lengths in $Ni(CO)_4$, $Co(NO)(CO)_3$ and $Fe(NO)_2(CO)_2$ are $1{\cdot}82 \pm 0{\cdot}03$, $1{\cdot}83 \pm 0{\cdot}02$ and $1{\cdot}84 \pm 0{\cdot}02$; and the CO bond lengths are $1{\cdot}15 \pm 0{\cdot}02$, $1{\cdot}14 \pm 0{\cdot}03$ and $1{\cdot}15 \pm 0{\cdot}03$ Å. The last three figures suggest strongly that the CO bond order in all three molecules is $2\frac{1}{2}$. This is confirmed by the CO stretching frequencies observed in the infra-red spectra. The values are: $Ni(CO)_4$, 2057 cm^{-1}; $Co(NO)(CO)_3$, 2047, 2011; $Fe(NO)_2(CO)_2$, 2083, 2034; $Mn(NO)_3CO$, 2088. Reference to Fig. 22 shows that the order, in all these compounds, is close to $2\frac{1}{2}$ for the CO bond.

The NO bond lengths in $Co(NO)(CO)_3$ and $Fe(NO)_2(CO)_2$ are $1{\cdot}14 \pm 0{\cdot}03$ and $1{\cdot}12 \pm 0{\cdot}03$ Å. The metal-nitrogen bond lengths are the same in both molecules; $1{\cdot}76 \pm 0{\cdot}03$ and $1{\cdot}77 \pm 0{\cdot}02$ respectively. The NO vibration frequencies are: $Co(CO)_3(NO)$, 1822 cm^{-1}; $Fe(CO)_2(NO)_2$, 1810, 1766; $Mn(CO)(NO)_3$, 1823, 1734 cm^{-1}. Comparison with the figures of section 5.4 and sections 6.6 and 6.7 suggests strongly that the NO bond order is close to $2\frac{1}{2}$, though it might be a little less, particularly in the manganese compound.

The structure of the cobalt compound is therefore

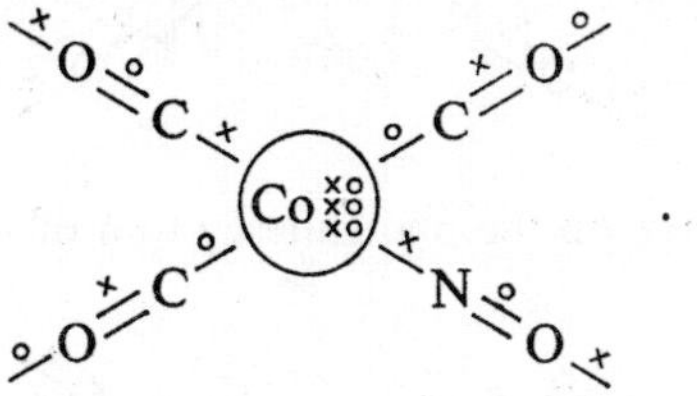

The formal charge on the cobalt atom is -3, whereas that on the nickel atom in $Ni(CO)_4$ is, with the corresponding formula, -2. However, the nickel atom has adjacent to it four carbon atoms having formal charges of zero but a higher electronegativity. In the cobalt compound one of the carbon atoms is replaced by a nitrogen atom having a formal charge of $+1$ and a still higher electronegativity.

The structure of the iron compound is primarily

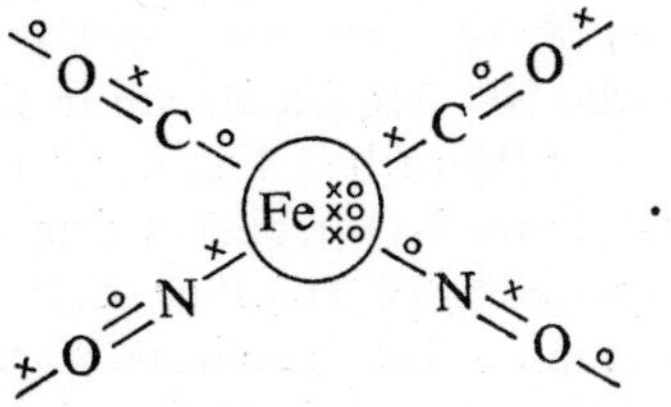

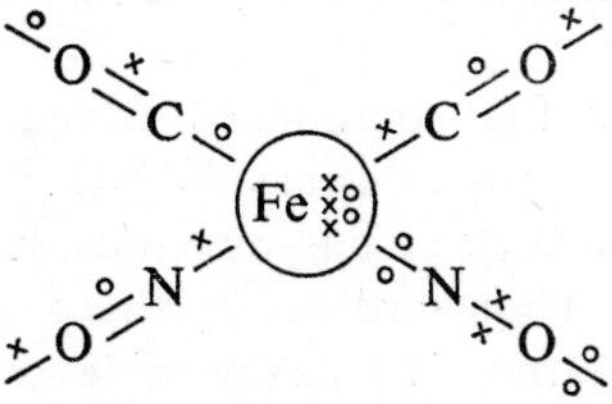

However, in this, the iron atom has a formal charge of -4 and, even though now two carbon atoms have been replaced by two nitrogen atoms, this high formal charge may give some importance to structures of the type in which the formal charge on the iron atom is reduced to $-3\frac{1}{2}$. The manganese compound will be expected to be primarily

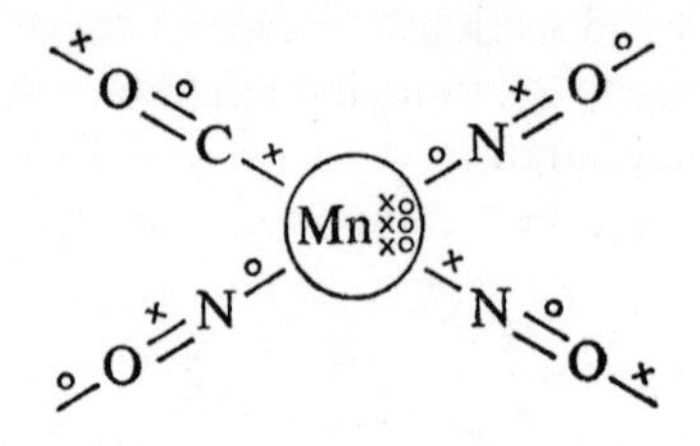

with a formal charge on the manganese atom of -5, but structures of the type

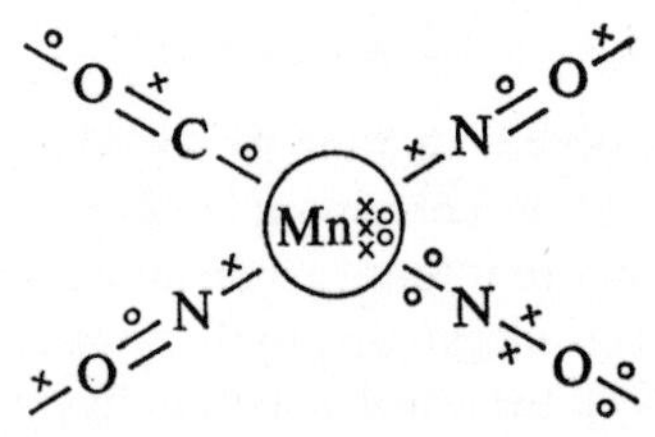

appear also to make some contribution. This reduces the formal charge on the manganese atom to $-4\frac{1}{2}$ and reduces slightly the order of the NO bond.

In $Fe(CO)_2(NO)_2$ the NO frequencies are in the neighbourhood of 1800 cm^{-1}. When one of the carbonyl groups is replaced by $(C_6H_5)_3P$, $(C_6H_5)_3As$ or $(C_6H_5)_3Sb$ the NO frequency drops to about 1750 cm^{-1} and when two are replaced by $(C_6H_5)_3P$ or $(C_6H_5)As$ it drops to about 1700 cm^{-1}. This must mean that these ligands are less good acceptors of electrons than is carbon monoxide so that structures containing

$$\mathrm{M} \overset{\times}{\underset{\times}{-}} \mathrm{N} \overset{\circ}{\underset{\circ}{-}} \mathrm{O} \overset{\times}{\underset{\times}{-}},$$

which transfer more charge away from the metal atom, become more important.

A most interesting four-coordinated complex is $Fe(NO)_4$. The infra-red spectrum shows that this has the NO frequencies: 1810, 1730 and 1140 cm^{-1}. This suggests an unsymmetrical structure in which three of the NO groups have a bond order of $2\frac{1}{2}$ (freq.: 1810 and 1730) and one has a bond order of $1\frac{1}{2}$ (freq. 1140). A possible structure is

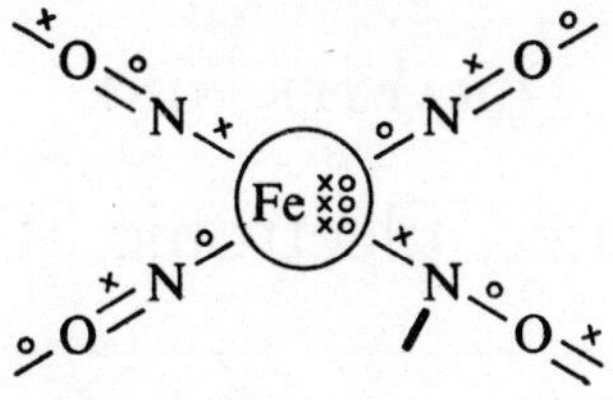

However, a more definite decision must await more structural evidence; in particular the shape and dimensions of the molecule (Rosenberg and Linnett, *A.C.S. Meeting*, 1963).

It is interesting that NO, CN^- and CO all combine with metal atoms in complexes, but that N_2, iso-electronic with CN^- and CO, does not. The reason for this is, that in the structures

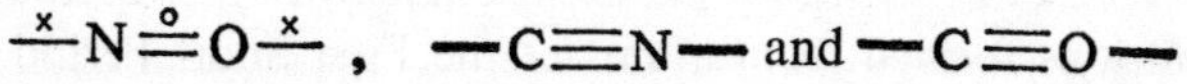

$$-N{=}O- \,, \quad -C{\equiv}N- \text{ and } -C{\equiv}O-$$

the atom which is ultimately attached to the metal atom carries a formal negative charge. In N_2 the formal charge on both atoms is zero.

CHAPTER NINE

Excited Electronic States

9.1 Introduction

In section 3.2, the electronic structures of the first two excited states of the oxygen molecule were described in terms similar to that used for the ground state. The results were summarized in Table 2 on page 41. This method made it possible to understand the sequence of the energies of the three states. In the first part of this chapter a similar formulation will be used to describe the low-lying excited states of other diatomic molecules and ions formed from atoms of the First Short Period. As was stated in section 3.8, these representations of the electronic structures correspond closely to the molecular orbital description, transformation to a more localized set of orbitals having been carried out (i.e. to a set of *equivalent* orbitals). The other sections of this chapter will deal with the excited states of some simple tri- and tetra-atomic species, with some theoretical calculations that have been carried out for the allyl radical and its positive and negative ions, and with some organic molecules recently studied by Brand, Callomon and their co-workers.

9.2 Diatomic Molecules

Table 7, which is analogous to Table 2 on page 41, lists some data for the ground and a number of identifiable excited states of the molecules C_2, N_2, N_2^+, O_2, O_2^+, CN, CO, CO^+ and NO. The symbol describing the symmetry of the total electronic wave function is given in the first column; this is followed by a summary of the occupation of the molecular orbitals (i.e. this column summarizes the simple molecular orbital description). The next two columns give the equilibrium bond length (in Ångstroms) and the force constant (in milli-dynes per Ångstrom) of the various states. These quantities are related to the level of bonding in each state (i.e. to the number of bonding electrons and nature of the orbitals they occupy). Convenient standards for the bond lengths are: CC, 1·54; NN, 1·40; OO, 1·32; CN, 1·48; CO, 1·47 and NO, 1·37 Å. For the homopolar molecules these are the sum of Pauling's single-bond radii, and for the heteropolar molecules values which bring the results for these heteropolar molecules to the same scale as that for homopolar molecules (see Linnett, *J.C.S.*, 1956). The corresponding figures for the force constants are: CC, 4·7; NN, 6·0; OO, 7·5; CN, 4·9; CO, 4·4 and NO, 6·3. These help in the rough assessment of bond order, since the length of four- and six-electron bonds are approximately 85% and 75% of the length of two-electron bonds (Pauling). The corresponding figures for the force constants are very roughly 200% and 400%. The last two columns summarize the disposition of the electrons, the two spin-sets being portrayed separately. In addition, in the last two columns, there are also listed the symmetry of the orbitals (σ or π) occupied by the *bonding* electrons. Thus the last two columns describe the number of electrons associated with the bond and with each atom.

In some cases, as in the very first state listed ($^1\Sigma_u^+$ of C_2), the electron distribution is such that there is just one electron associated with the atoms rather than with the bond. In such a case, two distributions should be combined with equal weight (e.g. $\circ\mathrm{C}\overset{\circ}{\underset{\circ}{:}}\mathrm{C}$ and $\mathrm{C}\overset{\circ}{\underset{\circ}{:}}\mathrm{C}\circ$ for the $^1\Sigma_u^+$ state of C_2); because of a shortage of space only one has been given in the Table 7, but an equal contribution of the second is implied.

An examination of the table will show that there is no case in which there are more than eight electrons in the shell of any atom; moreover there is no case in which there are more than four of either spin. This is a consequence of the fact that all the states considered are low-lying energetically, and so all of the electrons are occupying orbitals derived from atomic orbitals for which $n = 2$; they are either atomic, or shared between the two atoms. In a number of cases there are only seven, six or even five electrons ($^3\Pi_g$ state of C_2) in the vicinity of a particular atom.

Consider the states of O_2 and O_2^+. Those in which the bonds contain two electrons have $r_e = 1{\cdot}42$ or greater and k less than $3\frac{1}{2}$; those with three-electron bonds have r_e in the range 1·28 to 1·41 and k between $3\frac{1}{2}$ and 7; those with four electrons have r_e in the neighbourhood of 1·22 and k between 9 and 12; the state of O_2^+ containing a five-electron bond has $r_e = 1{\cdot}12$ and $k = 16{\cdot}6$. The length and strength of the bonds fall into the correct sequence therefore, though the variation in the strength of bonds of a given order is considerable. This variation arises from changes in the precise electron distribution and in the orbitals occupied by the bonding electrons. This has been analysed in more detail by the author elsewhere (*J.C.S.*, 1956); however, such a lengthy analysis would not be suitable here. It is interesting that the percentage variation in length and

TABLE 7

State	M.O. description	r_e	k	Disposition of electrons	
				One spin set	Other spin set
C_2 molecule					
$^1\Sigma_u^+$	$\sigma_g^2\sigma_u\pi_u^4\sigma_g$	1·24	11·8	$\times C\substack{\times\\\times}C\times$ (π^2)	$\circ C\substack{\circ\\\circ\\\circ}C$ ($\sigma\pi^2$)
$^1\Pi_g$	$\sigma_g^2\sigma_u\pi_u^3\sigma_g^2$	1·27	11·6	$\times C\substack{\times\\\times}C\times$ ($\sigma\pi$)	$\circ C\substack{\circ\\\circ\\\circ}C$ ($\sigma\pi^2$)
$^1\Pi_u$	$\sigma_g^2\sigma_u^2\pi_u^3\sigma_g$	1·32	9·1	$\times C\substack{\times\\\times}C\times$ (π^2)	$\circ C\substack{\circ\\\circ}C\circ$ ($\sigma\pi$)
$^1\Sigma_g^+$	$\sigma_g^2\sigma_u^2\pi_u^4$	1·24	12·2	$\times C\substack{\times\\\times}C\times$ (π^2)	$\circ C\substack{\circ\\\circ}C\circ$ (π^2)
$^3\Pi_g$	$\sigma_g^2\sigma_u^2\pi_u^2\sigma_g\pi_g$	1·54	4·3	$\substack{\times\\\times}C\times C\substack{\times\\\times}$ (σ)	$\circ C\circ C\circ$ (π)
$^3\Pi_g$	$\sigma_g^2\sigma_u\pi_u^3\sigma_g^2$	1·27	11·3	$\times C\substack{\times\\\times\\\times}C\times$ ($\sigma\pi^2$)	$\circ C\substack{\circ\\\circ}C$ ($\sigma\pi$)
$^3\Pi_u$	$\sigma_g^2\sigma_u^2\pi_u^3\sigma_g$	1·31	9·5	$\times C\substack{\times\\\times\\\times}C\times$ ($\sigma\pi^2$)	$\circ C\circ C\circ$ (π)
N_2 molecule					
$^3\Pi_u$	$\sigma_g^2\sigma_u\pi_u^4\sigma_g^2\pi_g$	1·15	17·1	$\substack{\times\\\times}N\substack{\times\\\times}N\substack{\times\\\times}$ ($\sigma\pi$)	$\circ N\substack{\circ\\\circ\\\circ}N$ ($\sigma\pi^2$)
$^3\Pi_g$	$\sigma_g^2\sigma_u^2\pi_u^4\sigma_g\pi_g$	1·21	12·4	$\substack{\times\\\times}N\substack{\times\\\times}N\substack{\times\\\times}$ ($\sigma\pi$)	$\circ N\substack{\circ\\\circ}N\circ$ (π^2)
$^3\Sigma_u^+$	$\sigma_g^2\sigma_u^2\pi_u^3\sigma_g^2\pi_g$	1·29	8·8	$\substack{\times\\\times}N\substack{\times\\\times}N\substack{\times\\\times}$ ($\sigma\pi$)	$\circ N\substack{\circ\\\circ}N\circ$ ($\sigma\pi$)
$^1\Pi_g$	$\sigma_g^2\sigma_u^2\pi_u^4\sigma_g\pi_g$	1·21	11·8	$\times N\substack{\times\\\times\\\times}N\times$ ($\sigma\pi^2$)	$\substack{\circ\\\circ}N\circ N\substack{\circ\\\circ}$ (π)
$^1\Sigma_g^+$	$\sigma_g^2\sigma_u^2\pi_u^4\sigma_g^2$	1·09	23·0	$\times N\substack{\times\\\times\\\times}N\times$ ($\sigma\pi^2$)	$\circ N\substack{\circ\\\circ\\\circ}N\circ$ ($\sigma\pi^2$)
N_2^+ ion					
$^2\Sigma_u^+$	$\sigma_g^2\sigma_u\pi_u^4\sigma_g^2$	1·08	24·2	$\times N\substack{\times\\\times\\\times}N\times$ ($\sigma\pi^2$)	$\circ N\substack{\circ\\\circ\\\circ}N$ ($\sigma\pi^2$)
$^2\Sigma_g^+$	$\sigma_g^2\sigma_u^2\pi_u^4\sigma_g$	1·12	20·1	$\times N\substack{\times\\\times\\\times}N\times$ ($\sigma\pi^2$)	$\circ N\substack{\circ\\\circ\\\circ}N\circ$ (π^2)
O_2 molecule					
$^3\Sigma_u^-$	$\sigma_g^2\sigma_u^2\pi_u^3\sigma_g^2\pi_g^3$	1·60	2·3	$\substack{\times\\\times\\\times}O\times O\substack{\times\\\times\\\times}$ (σ)	$\substack{\circ\\\circ\\\circ}O\circ O\circ$ (σ)
$^3\Sigma_u^+$	$\sigma_g^2\sigma_u^2\pi_u^3\sigma_g^2\pi_g^3$	1·42	3·2	$\substack{\times\\\times\\\times}O\times O\substack{\times\\\times\\\times}$ (σ)	$\substack{\circ\\\circ}O\circ O\substack{\circ\\\circ}$ (σ)
$^1\Sigma_g^+$	$\sigma_g^2\sigma_u^2\pi_u^4\sigma_g^2\pi_g^2$	1·23	9·7	$\substack{\times\\\times}O\substack{\times\\\times}O\substack{\times\\\times}$ ($\sigma\pi$)	$\substack{\circ\\\circ}O\substack{\circ\\\circ}O\substack{\circ\\\circ}$ ($\sigma\pi$)
$^1\Delta_g$	$\sigma_g^2\sigma_u^2\pi_u^4\sigma_g^2\pi_g^2$	1·22	10·7	$\substack{\times\\\times}O\substack{\times\\\times}O\substack{\times\\\times}$ ($\sigma\pi$)	$\substack{\circ\\\circ}O\substack{\circ\\\circ}O\substack{\circ\\\circ}$ ($\sigma\pi$)
$^3\Sigma_g^-$	$\sigma_g^2\sigma_u^2\pi_u^4\sigma_g^2\pi_g^2$	1·21	11·8	$\substack{\times\\\times\\\times}O\times O\substack{\times\\\times\\\times}$ (σ)	$\circ O\substack{\circ\\\circ\\\circ}O\circ$ ($\sigma\pi^2$)

TABLE 7—*continued*

State	M.O. description	r_e	k	Disposition of electrons: One spin set	Disposition of electrons: Other spin set
O_2^+ ion					
$^4\Sigma_g^-$	$\sigma_g^2\sigma_u^2\pi_u^4\sigma_g\pi_g^2$	1·28	6·7	$\substack{\times\\\times\\\times}O\times O\substack{\times\\\times\\\times}$ (σ)	$\circ O\substack{\circ\\\circ}O\circ$ (π^2)
$^2\Pi_u$	$\sigma_g^2\sigma_u^2\pi_u^3\sigma_g^2\pi_g^2$	1·41	3·8	$\substack{\times\\\times}O\substack{\times\\\times}O\substack{\times\\\times}$ $(\sigma\pi)$	$\substack{\circ\\\circ}O\circ O\substack{\circ\\\circ}$ (σ)
$^4\Pi_u$	$\sigma_g^2\sigma_u^2\pi_u^3\sigma_g^2\pi_g^2$	1·38	5·1	$\substack{\times\\\times\\\times}O\times O\substack{\times\\\times\\\times}$ (σ)	$\circ O\substack{\circ\\\circ}O\circ$ $(\sigma\pi)$
$^2\Pi_g$	$\sigma_g^2\sigma_u^2\pi_u^4\sigma_g^2\pi_g$	1·12	16·6	$\substack{\times\\\times}O\substack{\times\\\times}O\substack{\times\\\times}$ $(\sigma\pi)$	$\circ O\substack{\circ\\\circ\\\circ}O\circ$ $(\sigma\pi^2)$
CN radical					
$^2\Sigma^+$	$\sigma_1^2\sigma_2\pi_1^4\sigma_3^2$	1·15	17·8	$\times C\substack{\times\\\times\\\times}N\times$ $(\sigma\pi^2)$	$C\substack{\circ\\\circ\\\circ}N\circ$ $(\sigma\pi^2)$
$^2\Pi_i$	$\sigma_1^2\sigma_2^2\pi_1^3\sigma_3^2$	1·23	12·5	$\times C\substack{\times\\\times\\\times}N\times$ $(\sigma\pi^2)$	$\circ C\substack{\circ\\\circ}N\circ$ $(\sigma\pi)$
$^2\Sigma^+$	$\sigma_1^2\sigma_2^2\pi_1^4\sigma_3$	1·17	16·3	$\times C\substack{\times\\\times\\\times}N\times$ $(\sigma\pi^2)$	$\circ C\substack{\circ\\\circ}N\circ$ (π^2)
CO molecule					
$^3\Sigma^+$	$\sigma_1^2\sigma_2^2\pi_1^3\sigma_3^2\pi_2$	1·36	6·0	$\substack{\times\\\times}C\substack{\times\\\times}O\substack{\times\\\times}$ $(\sigma\pi)$	$\circ C\substack{\circ\\\circ}O\circ$ $(\sigma\pi)$
$^3\Pi_r$	$\sigma_1^2\sigma_2\pi_1^4\sigma_3^2\pi_2$	1·21	12·2	$\substack{\times\\\times}C\substack{\times\\\times}O\substack{\times\\\times}$ $(\sigma\pi)$	$C\substack{\circ\\\circ\\\circ}O\circ$ $(\sigma\pi^2)$
$^1\Pi$	$\sigma_1^2\sigma_2\pi_1^4\sigma_3^2\pi_2$	1·24	9·3	$\times C\substack{\times\\\times\\\times}O\times$ $(\sigma\pi^2)$	$\circ C\substack{\circ\\\circ}O\substack{\circ\\\circ}$ $(\sigma\pi)$
$^1\Sigma^+$	$\sigma_1^2\sigma_2^2\pi_1^4\sigma_3^2$	1·13	19·0	$\times C\substack{\times\\\times\\\times}O\times$ $(\sigma\pi^2)$	$\circ C\substack{\circ\\\circ\\\circ}O\circ$ $(\sigma\pi^2)$
CO^+ ion					
$^2\Sigma^+$	$\sigma_1^2\sigma_2^2\pi_1^4\sigma_3$	1·17	12·1	$\times C\substack{\times\\\times\\\times}O\times$ $(\sigma\pi^2)$	$\circ C\substack{\circ\\\circ}O\circ$ (π^2)
$^2\Pi_i$	$\sigma_1^2\sigma_2^2\pi_1^3\sigma_3^2$	1·24	9·9	$\times C\substack{\times\\\times\\\times}O\times$ $(\sigma\pi^2)$	$\circ C\substack{\circ\\\circ}O\circ$ $(\sigma\pi)$
$^2\Sigma^+$	$\sigma_1^2\sigma_2\pi_1^4\sigma_3^2$	1·12	19·8	$\times C\substack{\times\\\times\\\times}O\times$ $(\sigma\pi^2)$	$C\substack{\circ\\\circ\\\circ}O\circ$ $(\sigma\pi^2)$
NO molecule					
$^2\Pi_r$	$\sigma_1^2\sigma_2^2\pi_1^3\sigma_3^2\pi_2^2$	(1·4)	4·7	$\substack{\times\\\times}N\substack{\times\\\times}O\substack{\times\\\times}$ $(\sigma\pi)$	$\substack{\circ\\\circ}N\circ O\substack{\circ\\\circ}$ (σ)
$^2\Pi$	$\sigma_1^2\sigma_2^2\pi_1^4\sigma_3^2\pi_2$	1·15	15·9	$\substack{\times\\\times}N\substack{\times\\\times}O\substack{\times\\\times}$ $(\sigma\pi)$	$\circ N\substack{\circ\\\circ\\\circ}O\circ$ $(\sigma\pi^2)$

force constant is greater for bonds of low order than for those of high order.

A similar examination of the states of N_2 shows that for bonds containing six electrons $r_e = 1{\cdot}08$ or $1{\cdot}09$ and $k = 23$ or 24; for those containing five electrons $r_e = 1{\cdot}12$–$1{\cdot}15$ and $k = 17$–20; for those containing four electrons $r_e = 1{\cdot}21$–$1{\cdot}29$ and $k = 8{\cdot}8$–$12{\cdot}4$.

In C_2 there is a greater overlap in the lengths and strengths of the four- and five-electron bonds. In particular the ${}^1\Sigma_g^+$ state, in which the bonding group of electrons is π^4, has an unexpectedly short and strong bond. In CO and CO^+, the six-electron bonds have $r_e = 1{\cdot}12$ or $1{\cdot}13$ and $k = 19$ or 20; the five-electron bonds have $r_e = 1{\cdot}17$ to $1{\cdot}24$ and $k = 9{\cdot}3$ to $12{\cdot}2$;

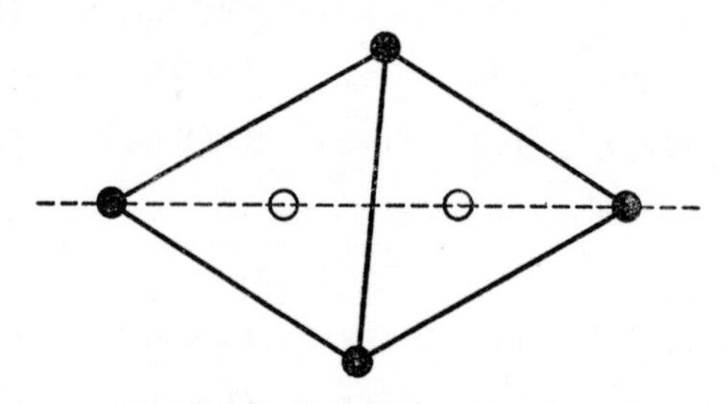

FIG. 23. Four electrons disposed as two triangles with a common edge between the nuclei; cf. O_2^+, ${}^4\Pi_u$ state, spin-set; ∘ O ⁘ O ∘ ($\sigma\pi$).

the ${}^3\Sigma^+$ state has a four-electron bond and $r_e = 1{\cdot}36$ and $k = 6$. So again the broad pattern is correct.

It is not possible in this section to discuss the disposition of electrons of all the thirty-five states in Table 7. For illustration, the states of O_2^+ will be selected because the known states of this ion contain spin-sets of four, five, six and seven electrons. The ${}^2\Pi_g$ (ground) state is similar to that of NO which was discussed in section 3.4. The ${}^4\Pi_u$ state has one spin-set of seven electrons disposed in the arrangement of highest probability near the corners of a pair of tetrahedra with a common apex between the nuclei (see Fig. 15). The electrons of the other spin-set of four are situated near the corners of two triangles having a common edge between the nuclei. This is illustrated in Fig. 23. The next state (${}^2\Pi_u$) has six electrons of one spin-set disposed near the corners of two tetrahedra with a common edge between the nuclei (see Fig. 16). The five of the other spin-set are at or near the corners of two triangles with a common apex between the nuclei. This is illustrated in Fig. 24. The fourth state ($^4\Sigma_g^-$) has seven electrons of one spin-set disposed near the corners of two tetrahedra with a common apex (as in Fig. 15). The four of the other spin-set are near the corners of two triangles with a common edge in the region between the nuclei. The arrangement of the two triangles is different from that shown in Fig. 23, and is illustrated in Fig. 25.

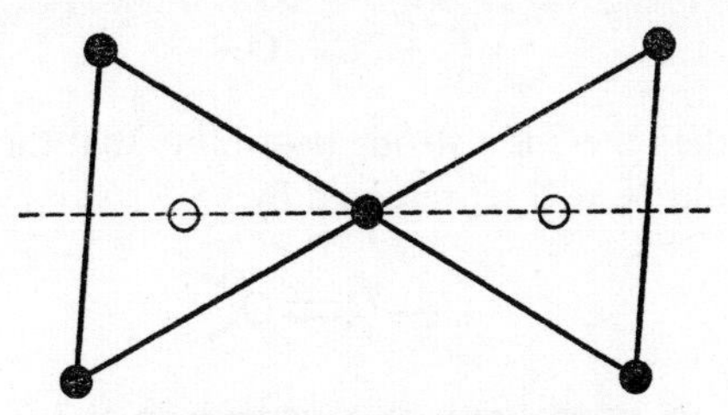

FIG. 24. Five electrons disposed as two triangles with a common apex between the nuclei, cf. O_2^+, $^2\Pi_u$ state, spin-set: $\genfrac{}{}{0pt}{}{\circ}{\circ}$ O ∘ O $\genfrac{}{}{0pt}{}{\circ}{\circ}$ (σ).

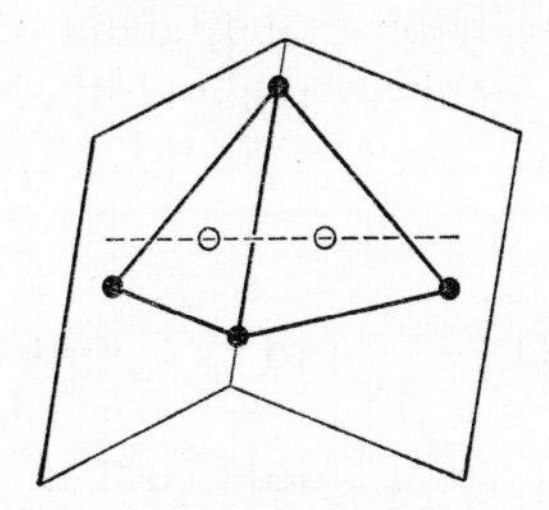

FIG. 25. Four electrons disposed as two triangles with a common edge; cf. O_2^+, $^4\Sigma_g^-$ state, spin-set: ∘ O $\genfrac{}{}{0pt}{}{\circ}{\circ}$ O ∘ (π^2). In this arrangement, which differs from that in Fig. 23, the common edge between the two triangles does not cut the line joining the nuclei.

As stated earlier the description of the electron disposition used here is derived directly from the molecular orbital formulation. However, because it is a localized description, it enables the disposition of the electrons relative to one another to be appreciated more easily. It is for this reason that Mason, Vanderslice, Maisch and Lippincott (*J.C.P.*, 1959, 1960) have found this type of description of value in calculating the potential energy curves of diatomic molecules both for ground and excited states.

9.3 Nitrosyl Compounds

Johnston and Bertin (*J. Mol. Sp.*, 1959), from their studies of the spectrum of nitrosyl fluoride, concluded that the NF bond is shorter and stronger in the excited state than in the ground state, but that, for the NO bond, the reverse change takes place. If the ground state structure is

$$\overset{\times}{-}\overset{|}{\underset{|}{F}} \circ N \overset{\times}{=} O \overset{\circ}{-}$$

(cf. section 5.4) then there is a strong possibility that the structure of the excited state would be well represented by

$$-\overset{|}{\underset{|}{F}}-\underset{|}{N}=O\lessdot \,.$$

This interpretation agrees with the increase in the NF characteristic frequency from 766 to 1086 cm^{-1} on excitation and with the decrease in that of NO from 1844 to 1450 cm^{-1}. It might have been expected that the NO frequency would be a little larger than this (perhaps 1500–1550 cm^{-1}) but the decrease is certainly about what would be expected.

J. Mason reports that for nitrosyl chloride the NO frequency falls from 1799 to 1580 cm^{-1} on excitation (*J.C.S.*, 1957). This agrees very well with a change from

$$\overset{\times}{-}\overset{|}{\underset{|}{Cl}} \circ \underset{|}{N} \overset{\times}{=} O \overset{\circ}{-} \qquad \text{to} \qquad -\overset{|}{\underset{|}{Cl}}-\underset{|}{N}=O\lessdot$$

on excitation. J. Mason has also deduced that, for CF_3NO, C_3F_7NO CCl_3NO etc., the NO frequency falls from about 1600 cm^{-1} to 1350 or 1400 cm^{-1} on excitation. This suggests a change from a ground state structure

$$F-\overset{\overset{F}{|}}{\underset{\underset{F}{|}}{C}}-\underset{|}{N}=O\lessdot$$

to one involving a three-electron NO bond. It is possible that this might be

$$F-\overset{\overset{-\overset{|\bullet}{F}-}{\bullet}}{\underset{\underset{F}{|}}{C}} \overset{\bullet}{-} \underset{|}{N} \overset{\bullet}{-} \underset{|}{\dot{O}}\bullet$$

but this requires more evidence from other frequencies (cf. the discussion of propenal and propynal in section 9.5).

9.4 Acetylene

Ingold and King, from their analysis of the 2200-Å band system of acetylene, concluded that the excited state has a 'zig-zag' configuration and that the CC and CH bond lengths are 1·383 and 1·09 Å respectively (*J.C.S.*, 1953). It is interesting that the electronic excitation produces this change of shape, and that the CC bond changes from a six- to a three-electron one having the same bond length as that in benzene. An examination of the electronic excitation involved, in terms of a molecular orbital description, suggests that the electronic structure would be represented best by a combination of the wave functions corresponding to

$$\begin{array}{ccc} & & \mathrm{H} \\ {}^{+\circ} & & {}^{+\circ} \\ & \mathrm{C} \; {}^{\circ}_{\circ} \times \mathrm{C}_{+} & \\ {}^{\circ}_{+} & & \\ \mathrm{H} & & \end{array} \quad \text{and} \quad \begin{array}{ccc} & & \mathrm{H} \\ {}^{+} & & {}^{+\circ} \\ & \mathrm{C} \; {}^{\circ}_{\circ} \times \mathrm{C} & \\ {}^{\circ}_{+} & & {}^{\circ +} \\ \mathrm{H} & & \end{array} .$$

Such a structure accounts both for the bond lengths and for the shape.

This structure is probably related to that of the ${}^{1}\Sigma_{u}^{-}$ state of N_2 (which is iso-electronic with C_2H_2). This would be

$$\circ \overset{\times}{\underset{\times}{}} \mathrm{N} \overset{\circ}{\underset{\circ}{\circ}} \times \mathrm{N} \overset{\times}{\underset{\times}{}} \circ \, .$$

In acetylene, however, two protons must also be bound to the central atoms. In the above structure of N_2 the electrons of the two spin-sets will not be well disposed to bind two protons, because one set would tend to bind them linearly (the circles), while the other would tend to make HCCH bent (the crosses). It would seem that a modification of the electronic system is made so that the two protons may be bound by electron pairs. However, this can only be achieved if one electron is displaced from the central bond, as otherwise the electronic pattern round the two carbon atoms of one spin-set (circles) would be very distorted from the ideal regular tetrahedral distribution. In other words, it is worth while to form two satisfactory electron-pair CH bonds, even though this means the removal of one electron from the central bond. Consequently the electronic structure is that already given and the surprising loss of *three* bonding electrons from the CC bond is accounted for (Linnett, *Can. J. of C.*, 1958).

9.5 Propynal and Propenal

Brand, Callomon and Watson (*Disc. F. S.*, 1963) have studied the absorption spectrum of propynal, HC≡C—CHO, in the near ultra-violet. They have been able to determine a number of vibration frequencies of the excited state. The excitation clearly has a major effect on the carbonyl group, as its characteristic frequency drops from about 1700 cm^{-1} to about 1300 cm^{-1}. But, also, the frequencies of the bending vibrations of the H—C≡C—C group change considerably showing that the electronic excitation has affected this part of the system as well. The C≡C characteristic frequency drops from about 2100 cm^{-1} to about 1950 cm^{-1}.

By using the rules relating bond length and force constant it has been concluded that the CO bond increases in length from 1·215 to 1·325 Å and the C≡C bond increases from 1·209 to 1·238. This suggests that the CO bond becomes a three-electron bond and that the CC becomes a five-electron bond. This would mean that the excitation can be interpreted as a change from

$$H-C\equiv C-\underset{\displaystyle H}{\underset{|}{C}}=\underset{|}{O}-$$

to

$$H-\overset{\circ}{C}\overset{\times}{\equiv}C\overset{\circ}{-}\underset{\displaystyle H}{\underset{|}{C}}\overset{\times}{-}\underset{|}{\overset{\circ}{O}}\times\ .$$

In effect, one of the electrons occupying a non-bonding orbital on the oxygen is excited into a CO anti-bonding orbital. In formaldehyde this means that the structure changes from

$$H-\underset{\displaystyle H}{\underset{|}{C}}=\underset{|}{O}- \quad \text{to} \quad H-\underset{\displaystyle H}{\underset{|}{\overset{\circ}{C}}}\overset{\times}{-}\underset{|}{\overset{\circ}{O}}\times\ .$$

This interpretation is supported by the observation that, in excited formaldehyde, the CO bond length is 1·32 Å. In propynal the same transition occurs but this effect is transmitted along the chain, in the manner shown, so that the CC bond is affected. In both cases the excitation is, on a molecular orbital formulation, of an electron from an orbital symmetrical to the plane of the molecule to one antisymmetrical to the plane. This is why it affects the electrons in the rest of the molecule differently in the excited from the way it does in the ground state.

In propenal, CH_2=CH—CHO, excitation lowers the CO characteristic frequency from 1723 to 1266 cm^{-1} and the C=C from 1625 to 1410 cm^{-1}. This shows that the excitation affects not only the CO bond but also the rest of the molecule (Brand and Williamson, *Disc. F.S.*, 1963). This is also shown by the changes in the bending frequencies of the CH_2=CH– part of the molecule. Another most significant change is that the excitation increases the resistance to torsion of the skeletal CCCO system; which is, in effect, a torsional motion about the central CC bond which is a single one in the ground state. By analogy with propynal the excitation would be interpreted as a change from

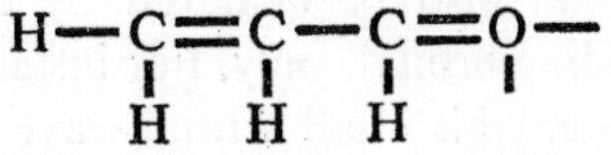

```
H—C=C—C=O—
   |  |  |   |
   H  H  H
```

to

```
   o  ×  o  × o
H—C—C—C—O×  .
   |  |  |   |
   H  H  H
```

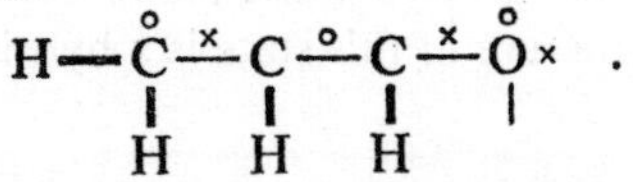

This explains the weakening of the CC and CO bonds and the increase in the resistance to torsional motion about the central CC bond.

In all the diagrams of this section, the electrons in the lower part of each formulae are in σ orbitals, and those in the upper part are in π orbitals (using a molecular orbital formulation). That is, for excited propenal,

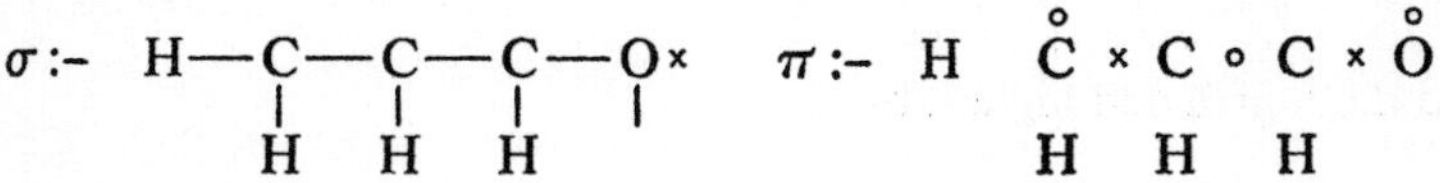

```
                                      o          o
σ :-  H—C—C—C—O×     π :-  H    C × C ∘ C × O
        |  |  |   |                 
        H  H  H                     H   H   H
```

but for the ground state

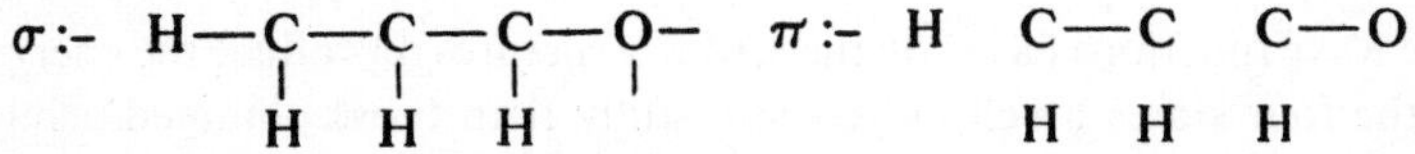

```
σ :-  H—C—C—C—O—     π :-  H    C—C    C—O
        |  |  |   |
        H  H  H                 H   H   H
```

However, in visualizing the total electron distribution, a separation into σ and π orbitals need not be maintained.

9.6 Allyl System

O. Sovers (Oxford) has carried out calculations for the ground and excited states of the electrons occupying the π orbitals of $C_3H_5^+$ (two), C_3H_5 (three) and $C_3H_5^-$ (four). D. M. Hirst (Oxford) showed that the ground state of $C_3H_5^+$ could be represented most successfully by structures of the type

$$CH_2 \overset{\times}{—} CH \overset{\circ}{—} CH_2 .$$

Placing the electron symbol (× or ∘) near one end of a bond implies that the bond orbital used employs an *unequal* contribution of the two atomic orbitals; the position indicates which atomic orbital makes the greater contribution. Sovers showed that a very good description of the excited states could also be achieved by employing *two-centre* bonding and anti-bonding orbitals only. For instance the wave function of the first excited state, which had a total wave function of the same symmetry as that of the ground state, could be obtained very well by supposing that the structure of this state is a hybrid of

$$CH_2 \overset{\bar{\times}}{—} CH \overset{\circ}{—} CH_2 \quad \text{and} \quad CH_2 \overset{\circ}{—} CH \overset{\bar{\times}}{—} CH_2 ,$$

where the bar over the cross indicates that it occupies an *anti-bonding* orbital. The next excited state of this symmetry class is represented by

$$CH_2 \overset{\bar{\times}\;\circ}{—} CH — CH_2 ,$$

and the fourth and highest by

$$CH_2 \overset{\bar{\circ}\,\bar{\times}}{—} CH — CH_2 .$$

The wave functions based on these four structures reproduce the energies of the four states much more successfully than those obtained using a simple molecular orbital treatment. The M.O. method of formulating wave function allows the electrons too high a chance of being near one another in the lower states, and too high a chance of being distant from one another in the upper state.

A similar treatment was successful for the four-electron system of $C_3H_5^-$. For this the ground state is

$$\overset{\times}{C}H_2 \overset{\circ}{—} CH \overset{\times}{—} \overset{\circ}{C}H_2$$

(cf. ozone). The structures of the three excited states of the same symmetry are

$$\text{1st} \quad \overset{\times}{C}H_2 \overset{\circ}{—} CH \overset{\bar{\times}}{—} \overset{\circ}{C}H_2 \qquad \text{and equivalent forms,}$$

$$\text{2nd} \quad \overset{\times}{\underset{}{\overset{\circ}{C}}}H_2 — CH \overset{\times\ \bar{\circ}}{—} CH_2 \qquad \text{and equivalent forms,}$$

$$\text{3rd} \quad \overset{\times}{\overset{\circ}{C}}H_2 — CH \overset{\bar{\circ}}{\overset{\times}{—}} CH_2 \qquad \text{and equivalent forms.}$$

(The equivalent forms are included to achieve the full symmetry.) Again the energies calculated were closer to those obtained using a full configuration interaction treatment than those calculated using simple molecular orbital functions. The allyl radical was also treated in the same way. For the details of these calculations, and the results, reference may be made to the original paper by Sovers and Linnett (*Disc. F.S.*, 1963).

CHAPTER TEN

Conclusion and Assessment

10.1 Wave Functions and Chemical Formulae

A chemical formula is intended to be a symbolic representation of the electronic wave function and electron distribution of a molecule. It is important therefore that there should be a well-defined connection between a symbol in a formula and the wave function, or part of the wave function to which the symbol relates. Thus the line representing a two-electron bond between two atoms is, in the simple valence-bond method which uses a Heitler–London procedure, related in an unambiguous way to a wave function. If this function needs to be improved by adding ionic terms, then the relationship is not so well defined but the line still represents clearly the type of function that is to be employed; it may be necessary to fix the value of some adjustable constant by the application of either the variation principle or intuition, but that is all.

In the present book, so far, because the treatment has been qualitative, this link between the formula and the wave function has not been clearly defined. To demonstrate that a clear connection exists, the wave function of He_2^+ corresponding to the formula

$$\overset{\times}{\text{He}} \circ \overset{\times}{\text{He}}$$

will be constructed. Let the atoms be labelled A and B. The formula implies that there are two electrons, with the same spin, occupying atomic orbitals on A and B, and one, with the opposite spin, occupying a bond orbital common to A and B. In the most simple procedure, the atomic orbitals used will be $1s_A$ and $1s_B$ and the bond orbital will be $(1s_A + 1s_B)$. The first two will be associated with say α-spin wave functions and the last with a β-spin wave function; the three electrons must be permuted among the three orbitals and the separate terms combined with the correct signs. If a more sophisticated function is required for calculating a property more exactly, this can be done by modifying the above function, and the form such modifications are to take can be laid down. Therefore it is possible to say that the formula defines the wave function.

This connection can be extended for application to more complex systems.

It is interesting that exponents of the molecular orbital method, which provides the clearest way for constructing molecular wave functions, have never felt the need to provide *chemical* formulae which illustrate and symbolize the wave functions. Recently, it might be said, this has been done, in a very limited manner, for aromatic systems such as those containing the benzene ring, by adding to the centre of the ring a circle which symbolizes the six electrons in occupation of the three lowest π orbitals. It is very probable that one of the reasons why molecular orbital treatments were accepted only slowly by experimental chemists was that theoreticians were unwilling to devise chemical formulae to represent their ideas. This was undoubtedly a pity because it lowered the chance that experimental chemists would themselves use their experimental knowledge for the successful development of this particular method.

In many chemical formulae that appear in books and papers, dotted lines are used to indicate or suggest some form of binding which is less than that of an electron pair. Sometimes the electron distribution or wave function that the dotted line is intended to represent is defined, but this is not always so. It seems to the author to be important and, in fact, to be basic to any treatment that can properly be called scientific, that any symbolism used in a chemical formula should illustrate, in as clear a way as is possible, an electron distribution and a wave function, and that the connection between them should be definable.

10.2 Localized and Delocalized Descriptions

The description and wave functions of diatomic and polyatomic molecules are all very approximate. Consequently, different methods of approaching this problem may be very different from one another at the present stage. However, it is to be hoped that, as different treatments are improved more and more, they will come to resemble one another more and more closely. In simple systems this situation exists already.

The different methods of formulating wave functions are of two types. Those which use localized orbitals, none of which embrace more than two (or perhaps three) atomic regions; and those which use delocalized orbitals, all of which spread over the whole region of the molecule. The second is known as the molecular orbital method. In its most simple form the disposition of the nuclear framework is assumed. Then the orbitals possible for a single electron in the field of this framework are calculated (often, the more tightly bound electrons are included with the framework). The derived orbitals are then arranged in the order of their energies and, for the ground state, the requisite number of electrons is added to fill the lowest possible set of orbitals; two electrons, one of each spin, are allowed to each orbital. This is the ordinary application of the 'building-up' principle employed in the manner that has been used for atoms for forty years.

This provides a procedure which has a great many advantages. It is very straightforward, and it takes full advantage of the symmetry of the system so that effects which are a consequence of the symmetry follow from it very directly and unambiguously. Also, if the wave function is made antisymmetric, by using a determinantal form, full account is taken of the Pauli Principle and of the effects of spin correlation, though such effects may not be easy to visualize with the wave function in its molecular orbital and determinantal form. However, it is possible to transform the molecular orbital function into one, which uses so-called equivalent orbitals, and these, if properly chosen, do make the effects of spin correlation clear. But the simple molecular orbital function does not allow at all for the effects of charge correlation. This is clearly the case because the molecular orbital function is constructed from a number of independent one-electron functions, each determined as if the other electrons were not there. As a result, all calculations made for ground states using a simple molecular orbital representation, over-estimate the magnitude of the mean inter-electron repulsion energy. However, as was pointed out in section 4.3, all simple treatments which make use of a simple basic description can be improved by mixing with the basic description, functions corresponding to other 'states' of the same system; this is called configuration interaction, but, when it is used, a simple visualization of the electron distribution becomes even more difficult.

Because of the dual effect of charge and spin correlation, it is a good approximation to regard the space associated with the molecule as divided into a number of regions. By the Pauli Principle it is impossible for there to be more than two electrons in the same region. In the ordinary valence-bond method, the space is divided into a number of regions which is half the number of electrons and two electrons are assigned to each region. These regions are associated either with one atom, and such an orbital is described as an unshared one, or with a pair of atoms (or in a few cases three) and then they may be regarded as bond regions. In the Heitler–London treatment the two electrons are kept apart within the bond region to a great extent, but it is correctly included along with this kind of treatment because it is one that is only suitable for pairs of electrons. Because the regions may be chosen so as to take account of inter-electron repulsion, and with Heitler–London functions for the bonds, some additional correlation is also included, the energy calculated using a valence-bond method is often better than that obtained using a molecular orbital treatment. However, the method does not so naturally take account of the whole molecule, so that the construction of the wave function is less straightforward and the treatment does not allow for the effect of the total molecular symmetry so directly.

As with the molecular orbital treatment, the wave function can often be improved considerably by mixing together wave functions which correspond to different structures; this device is called resonance. The various structures that are mixed differ from one another in the way the molecular space is divided into different regions. But in all the structures, with each region there is associated a pair of electrons.

The method proposed in this book is based on a localized approach but, instead of dealing always with the electrons in pairs, one of each spin, the space is divided into one set of regions for the electrons of one spin, and into another set of regions for the electrons of the other spin. If the two sets of regions are the same as each other then the electrons occupy the regions in pairs but, if they are not, and this is permitted, then the disposition of the electrons of one spin is different from that of the electrons of the other spin. It is this modification that makes this method different from the ordinary valence-bond method. However, it resembles the valence-bond method in employing as its basis a localized approach and, in this, it differs from the molecular orbital method. Calculations which have been carried out for a wide variety of species show that this method gives a more satisfactory description of the ground state of many systems than do either the ordinary valence bond or the molecular orbital methods.

A particular connection between this method and the valence-bond method of formulating structures is worth reiterating in somewhat more detail. Suppose that, for a given molecule, two Lewis–Pauling electron-paired structures are reasonable. Then the total structure will be described as a resonance hybrid of the two, and the electron distribution will be described by $(a\Psi_{\rm I}+b\Psi_{\rm II})^2 = a^2\Psi_{\rm I}^2+b^2\Psi_{\rm II}^2+2ab\Psi_{\rm I}\Psi_{\rm II}$. Clearly on the present hypothesis, a structure in which the electrons of one spin are disposed in the manner of one Lewis–Pauling structure and those of the other in the manner of the other will be possible (and, in fact, preferable). This structure is intermediate between the two electron-paired structures and so eliminates the extremes of the electron distribution (Ψ_{I}^2 and Ψ_{II}^2). It is this that, in many cases, provides the reason why the calculated energy is lower. However, for the *qualitative* application of the hypothesis, this feature presents a difficulty. For example, if a bond length is observed to be intermediate between that expected for bonds of order one and two, it is equally possible to account for this by saying that the structure is a hybrid of two Lewis–Pauling structures, or that it has the intermediate structure which does not involve spatial pairs. In most cases it would not be possible to make a choice between the two explanations on the basis of qualitative or semi-quantitative data. However, the calculations that have been carried out do show that in many radicals, molecules and ions the structure which disposes the electrons of each spin in different patterns is preferable; moreover it is possible to understand, on general grounds, why this is so.

10.3 Assessment

This book is not, and was never intended to be, the final word. The object has been threefold: (1) to state the hypothesis and show its basis and general mode of application; (2) to describe in detail a number of molecules and ions where, as shown by calculations or on more qualitative grounds, the proposal appears to have definite advantages; and (3) to indicate, by means of further examples, spheres in which this method will probably also be useful.

As regards (2), it seems clear that there are instances where this method provides a definite improvement over any other in the formulation of electronic structures. For instance, calculations have shown that, for ozone, the nitrite ion, benzene, butadiene, the allyl radical and positive and negative ions, diborane and other species, structures involving two-centre bonds containing an odd number of electrons, provide a better description of the electronic structure than do the simple molecular orbital and valence-bond descriptions. This can be tested. Also there are certain small molecules for which this approach provides a very satisfactory qualitative description. Examples are nitric oxide, including the fact that it does not dimerize, nitrogen dioxide, the low-lying states of the oxygen molecule including the ground state, the superoxide ion, carbon dioxide and iso-electronic species, the two kinds of nitroso-compounds, dioxygen difluoride, and there are others.

The success in this wide range of simple systems undoubtedly justifies a continued study of this method of formulating electronic structures.

In this book, in Chapter 7 for example, it was shown that the idea that had been developed for the small odd-electron species (NO, NO_2 etc.) could be extended, using the same concepts, to some of the larger organic free radicals: semiquinones, diphenyl nitric oxide, triphenylpicryl-hydrazyl, etc. Three regions in which further investigation will be required are (*a*) compounds containing atoms such as sulphur and phosphorus, for which it is probable that the valence shell can be expanded beyond the octet; (*b*) larger aromatic systems; (*c*) complex ions. Perhaps this method will not, in all cases, provide particular advantages relative to alternative ways of describing structures and constructing wave functions. However, this should not discourage the further investigation of the procedure as the wide variety of molecules and ions known to the chemist will undoubtedly require, for some time to come, a variety of treatments and ways of writing chemical formulae; some will be better in some cases, others will be preferable in others. A similar view has been expressed by Basolo and Pearson in their book. They said about the valence bond, molecular orbital and electrostatic theories: 'To begin with, certainly we are dealing in each case with an approximation that cannot be complete. All three approaches have their uses, and one or the other may be most convenient in any one application.'

As regards (*a*) above, the structures of several molecules and ions containing these elements were considered in sections 3, 4, 5, 6 and 7 in Chapter 8 and certain of their properties were adequately explained. However, there is the persistent difficulty which is going to be present whatever approach is employed, namely that the possibility of expanding the valence shell beyond the octet introduces a wider range of allowable structures and choosing the best becomes more difficult. As regards (*b*), the calculation that has been carried out for benzene, which shows that a description involving three-electron bonds is a good one, does suggest that a simplified study, probably involving initially ruthless approximations (cf. Hückel), would be interesting. As regards (*c*), nothing directly concerned with complex ions has been included in this book though the discussion of carbonyls and nitrosyls in sections 8.8 and 8.9 must involve similar problems. However, more work is needed here to show whether this method has a contribution to make.

There are two other fields in which this method might prove useful; these are (i) the structures of transition state complexes, and (ii) the structures of low-lying excited states of diatomic and fairly simple polyatomic molecules. Several organic reactions have been discussed in Chapters 6 and 7 and there is some indication that the method might prove valuable. At the present time H. C. Bowen (Oxford) is preparing to carry out some calculations for proton and hydrogen atom transfer. The results will help to show whether further studies in this direction are likely to be profitable. The examples presented in Chapter 9 suggest that a broader examination of the application of this method to excited states should be carried out, though the precise direction in which this should be developed is not yet clear.

To summarize, it seems not unfair to conclude from the contents of the first half of this book, and from the examination of the simple systems considered in Chapters 3, 4 and 5, that there are sound reasons for believing that the hypothesis is firmly based and that there are advantages in making use of it for formulating at least some molecular electronic structures. This, together with the examples presented in Chapters 6, 7, 8 and 9, provides justification for also believing that the hypothesis deserves further study and investigation.

APPENDIX

Bibliography

Other books which are particularly important in connection with the contents of this one are:

Special Publications of the Chemical Society, No. **11**. Tables of Interatomic Distances and Configurations in Molecules and Ions (1958). Edited by L. E. SUTTON. (Most of the bond-length data are taken from this compilation.)

BELLAMY, L. J. (1958). *Infra-red Spectra of Complex Molecules*. Methuen. (Most of the data on characteristic frequencies are from this book.)

HERZBERG, G. (1950). *Molecular Spectra and Molecular Structure of Diatomic Molecules*. New York: Van Nostrand Inc. (This was used for data on diatomic molecules.)

WELLS, A. F. (1962). *Structural Inorganic Chemistry*. Oxford University Press. (One or two interatomic distances were taken from this book.)

COTTRELL, T. L. (1958). *The Strengths of Chemical Bonds*. London, Butterworths. (Some bond energies were obtained from this book.)

WATERS, W. A. (1948). *Free Radicals*. Oxford University Press. (This was used for the experimental facts for Chapter 7.)

LEWIS, G. N. (1923). *Valence and the Structure of Atoms and Molecules*. New York: Chemical Catalog Co. (This book gives a general account of his proposals and ideas.)

SIDGWICK, N. V. (1929). *Electronic Theory of Valency*. Oxford University Press. (This made an important contribution in the period following the initial proposal of G. N. Lewis.)

PAULING, L. (1928, 1960). *Nature of the Chemical Bond*. Cornell University Press. (For general views and opinions on valency, resonance etc., and for the treatment of particular molecules and ions etc.)

The following abbreviations have been used in the text for Journals, etc.:

Adv. I. and R-C., Advances in Inorganic and Radiochemistry; *Ber.*, Berichte; *Can. J. of C.*, Canadian Journal of Chemistry; *Can. J. of P.*,

Canadian Journal of Physics; *Chem. and Ind.*, Chemistry and Industry; *Disc. F.S.*, Discussions of the Faraday Society; *J.A.C.S.*, Journal of the American Chemical Society; *J.C.P.*, Journal of Chemical Physics; *J.C.S.*, Journal of the Chemical Society; *J. Mol. Sp.*, Journal of Molecular Spectroscopy; *Nat.*, Nature; *Proc. C.S.*, Proceedings of the Chemical Society; *P.N.A.S.*, Proceedings of the National Academy of Sciences, U.S.A.; *Q.R.C.S.*, Quarterly Review of the Chemical Society; *T.F.S.*, Transactions of the Faraday Society; *Z. Naturf.*, Zeitscrift für Naturforschung; *Z. Phys.*, Zeitschrift für Physik.

Indexes

Subjects

Substances

Authors